The Journey of Al & Gebra to the Land of Algebra

Tucker, Bethanie H., Ed.D.
The Journey of Al & Gebra to the Land of Algebra.
Bethanie H. Tucker © 2005. x, 120 pp.
ISBN: 1-929229-43-7

Published by aha! Process, Inc.

Other books by Bethanie H. Tucker, Ed.D.

Tucker Signing Strategies for Reading
Mr. Base Ten Invents Mathematics

Bethanie H. Tucker, Ed.D.

The Journey of Al & Gebra to the Land of Algebra

Table of Contents

Acknowledgments

This book would not have been possible without the contributions of …

Dr. Ruby K. Payne, president and founder of aha! Process, Inc., for helping me understand the need for a mental model for algebra—and encouraging me to create this book.

Tonja Hudson, professor of mathematics at Averett University in Danville, Virginia, who critiqued each mental model and offered a world of helpful suggestions.

Dan Shenk, editor extraordinaire, who doesn't rest until every single word sounds right, looks right, and feels right.

Jesse Conrad, preliminary editor, whose deft touch smoothed out some of the rough places on Al and Gebra's ride through the kingdoms.

Frieda Probst, book designer, who made my document look inviting to young readers.

Peggy Conrad, vice president of publications for aha! Process, who turned a fledgling manuscript into a real book.

Four brilliant students (see photo below) at the Opportunity School in Danville, Virginia, who suggested, among other things, a medieval theme for the story, and the principal of the school, who arranged time for me to meet with the students.

Photo by Kenneth Bond, art director, Averett University

(From left) Ryan Jones, Kristen Terry, Demars Wilson, the author, and Greg Toy. Not pictured: Sammy Massie, Opportunity School principal.

Introduction

The story of Al and Gebra (pronounced JEH-bruh) provides a mental model for many basic algebraic concepts. A mental model is a way of holding abstract thought in our head.

Multiple readings of *The Journey of Al & Gebra to the Land of Algebra* will enable the reader to easily access the appropriate mental model for solving an algebra problem. For example, a student who needs to remember how to add positive and negative numbers can recall the chapter in *Al & Gebra* where the princess eats positive berries that make her grow and negative berries that make her shrink. Whichever she eats the most of determines the results. The student then would know how to solve the problem.

Al & Gebra's storyline is understandable by students as young as third or fourth grade, yet sophisticated enough for individuals in high school or beyond.

The Journey of Al & Gebra to the Land of Algebra is a starting point for learning algebra. It provides a foundation for concrete, logical, understanding of abstract thought. It is not intended to take the place of instructional programs that provide more detailed explanations and practice material.

Enjoy the journey!

The Departure

In a land of dragons and dungeons, queens and kings, lords and ladies, and moats and castles, there lived a young man and a young woman. Their names were Al and Gebra. When this story begins, Al and Gebra are kneeling before the king. His royal court is watching silently from behind the throne.

"Al and Gebra," the king said as he held the tip of his sword over their heads. "You have reached the age of adulthood, and you have been recommended for the ranks of Lord and Lady. But before I can bestow this honor upon you, you must prove yourselves worthy."

"How must we do this, Your Majesty?" Gebra asked without looking up.

"Your task will not be an easy one," the king answered. "You must travel to each of the 14 kingdoms in our great forest. You will discover that every kingdom is facing a serious problem. You must find an answer to each problem and bring the solutions back to me."

"We will do as you ask," Al promised as he and Gebra rose, bowed slightly, and silently exited the chamber.

"I hope so," the king whispered under his breath as he watched them depart.

The First Kingdom
Positive and Negative Numbers

The dark shadows of the First Kingdom loomed in the distance as Al and Gebra emerged from the forest. They approached the huge stone walls cautiously, pausing before the drawbridge.

"The Kingdom of Whole Numbers," Al read from the sign above the castle. "I wonder what that means."

"The people in this kingdom call themselves Whole Numbers," a squeaky voice whispered from the shadows.

"Who's there?" Gebra asked, her horse dancing nervously.

"Here I am!" Al and Gebra saw the bony arm of a small, thin woman waving at them from behind a huge rock.

"Why do the people in your kingdom call themselves Whole Numbers?" Al asked.

"Because we're all named after whole numbers: Zero, One, Two, Three, Fifty-nine, Seventy-two, Eighty-one, and so on. That's why." The tiny woman bobbed into full view as she talked.

Whole number: any of the numbers 0, 1, 2, 3, and so on

"But whole numbers make dumb names," she continued. "Who wants to be named 'Thirty-seven?' Or 'One hundred and six?' Or 'Two thousand and eighty?' I don't."

"You certainly are negative!" Gebra responded.

"That's me! Negative Number, at your service." The bony woman took a bow.

"Negative Number!" Al said with a laugh. "That does have a nicer ring to it than 'One hundred and six.' Does the Kingdom of Whole Numbers have a problem that needs to be solved?"

"Why don't you find out for yourself?" Negative Number snapped.

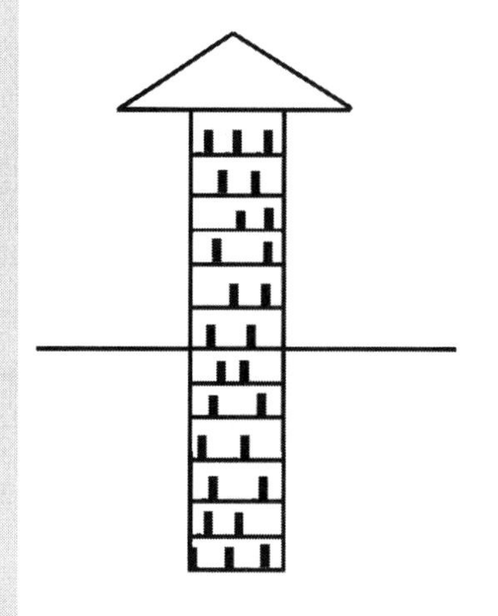

Al thought the tiny lady might be helpful in some way, so he said, "If you would like to come inside with us, you can ride with me on my horse."

Before anyone knew what had happened, the tiny lady was in the saddle, holding Al tightly around his waist. "Giddy-up!" she yelled, tapping the horse's sides with the heels of her narrow, pointed shoes.

Al's horse responded, and within seconds the party of three was entering the courtyard. Once inside Al and Gebra saw people running everywhere, many of them arguing with one another. "Why does everyone look so confused?" Gebra asked Negative Number, who was barely visible behind Al.

"Because we can't find our rooms," she said. Negative Number's voice sounded desperate.

"Some rooms are in the dungeon, and some are in the tower.

"Each of us knows the number of the floor that our room is on, but we don't know whether to go up into the tower or down into the dungeon to find it.

"For example, my room is on the fifth floor, but I don't know whether that's the fifth floor up, in the tower, or the fifth floor down, in the dungeon," Negative Number said, then fell silent.

"This is a serious problem," said Gebra. "We need to talk to someone in charge." So Gebra urged her horse toward a line of armored soldiers.

"Halt!" the soldiers' voices shouted when Al and Gebra were about 10 feet in front of them. Al's horse reared and Negative Number tumbled to the ground.

"Some way to show your gratitude!" she snarled at Al.

"Take us to your leader," Al demanded of the soldiers. In unison they lifted their right feet, then their lefts. Chanting and marching, the soldiers resembled a human door as the group parted down the middle. Finally the human door opened enough to reveal a queen sitting on a platinum throne.

"Her Majesty, Mean Queen Jean," a small boy announced through a megaphone.

Al and Gebra dismounted their horses, walked to the foot of the queen's throne, and bowed. "Your Majesty," they said before straightening up.

"If you don't mind my asking, why do the people of this kingdom call you *mean?"* Gebra asked. Al cleared his throat and glanced sideways at Gebra, questioning the propriety of posing such a question.

"It's simple," the queen replied. "They call me *mean* because I am average. I am the average height, average weight, and average age—and I have the average IQ of all the adults in the kingdom. *Mean* is another word for average, so they call me *mean."*

Mean: The arithmetic mean, often called the average or simply the mean, is the sum of the values divided by the total number of values.

Examples: The mean of 5, 7, and 9 is 7 ($5 + 7 + 9 = 21$; $21 \div 3 = 7$).
The mean of 1, 57, 100, and 2 is 40 ($1 + 57 + 100 + 2 = 160$; $160 \div 4 = 40$).

"Your Majesty, Mean Jean," Al said, bowing slightly. "We are in search of a problem to solve. Does your kingdom have any problems?"

A deafening roar of clanging armor filled the chamber as knights clasped their hands over their mouths, trying to stifle their roars of laughter.

"Silence!" the queen shouted, glaring at the knights, then looked back at Al and Gebra. "Yes," she said, "we have a problem, but why don't you just get a good night's sleep before we talk about it. Room numbers, please!"

The small boy disappeared into a nearby chamber, then reappeared with a large stone bowl, which he lifted up to Al and Gebra. "Your room numbers!" he said. Gebra looked inside the bowl and saw many small pieces of paper, with a numeral written on each one. She reached inside and took one piece of paper. "Number 12," she held the paper up for all to see.

"So," said the queen, "your room is on the twelfth floor. Now go to your room."

"But should I go to the twelfth floor up in the tower, or to the twelfth floor down in the dungeon? They're opposites!" Gebra's voice sounded tense.

"That's for you to figure out!" The queen sounded equally annoyed.

"That's the problem," the child whispered from somewhere near Gebra's elbow. "We don't know how to show whether the numbers mean that we should go up into the tower or down into the dungeon. All we know is that they're, well, numbers!"

"We need to think of something," Gebra whispered to Al.

"To begin with, the ground that we're standing on is the line that separates the tower from the dungeon. We can call this line 'zero,'" Al suggested.

"So I'm standing on zero. That's just what I thought," Negative Number mocked.

"Now we need a name for the numbers that are up in the tower," Gebra continued.

"If your room is in the tower, that would be positive," Al said. "So the numbers that are above zero can be called 'positive numbers.'"

Positive numbers: Numbers that are greater than zero are positive.

"Good idea. And numbers in the dungeon are less than zero. What should we call numbers that are less than zero?" Gebra wondered aloud.

"This is a waste of time," Negative Number grumbled.

"Negative Number, would you please stop being so negative?" Gebra said with a scowl, then smiled as an idea lit up her face. "That's it, Negative Number! We can call numbers that are less than zero 'negative numbers.'"

"Negative numbers are the opposite of positive numbers," Negative Number boasted.

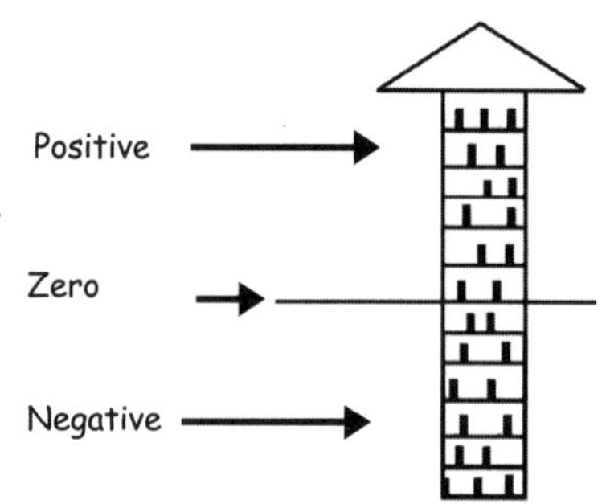

"So, if your room is in the dungeon," Al said to Gebra, "your room number is negative—negative twelve (-12). If it is in the tower, it is positive—positive twelve (+12)."

Negative numbers: Numbers that are less than zero are negative.

"I want to make a proclamation!" the queen said, rising from her throne. "We will no longer be called The Kingdom of Whole Numbers! From this day forward we will be called the Kingdom of Integers—whole numbers and their opposites."

Within minutes the sign above the drawbridge that had read "The Kingdom of Whole Numbers" was removed, and a new sign was put in its place:

The Kingdom of Integers: whole numbers and their opposites

All the integers in the kingdom lined up to have a positive (+) or a negative (-) sign drawn in front of the numbers on their room-assignment slips. By midnight everyone was tucked in bed and sound asleep. "You're a hero," Gebra whispered to Negative Number before heading up the stairs to her room on the +12th (positive twelfth) floor.

"That's right. From now on half of the numbers in the world will be named after you," Al added before going to his room on the -23rd (negative twenty-third) floor.

"Don't want to be a hero!" Negative Number shouted after them. "But I'll try," she added quietly, when they were out of hearing range.

The next morning Negative Number and the boy were waiting for Al and Gebra in the courtyard. "Look," Negative Number said excitedly, as she pointed to a drawing she had made in the sand. "If the tower were to fall down, this is what it would look like!"

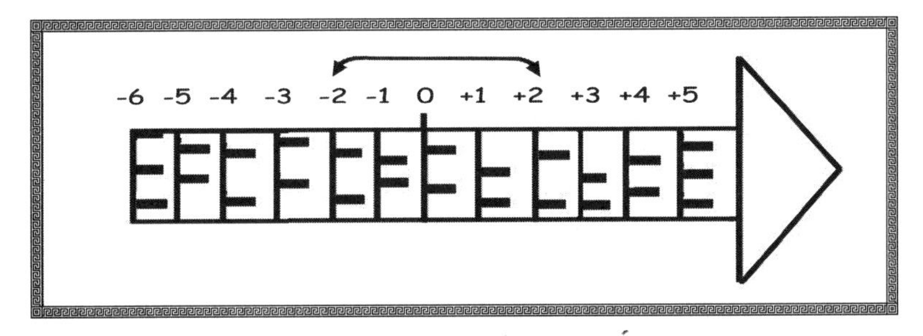

"And another thing," the lad said, pointing to the chart. "Positive 2 and negative 2 are the same distance from zero. So even though negative 2 is negative, it still means that someone must walk two floors from zero."

"You're right," Al said. "Negative numbers have value."

"Absolutely," the boy said.

Al smiled. "Good thinking," he said. "We'll say that the value of a negative number is its opposite, and we'll call that the 'absolute value.'"

"Absolutely," the boy repeated.

The absolute value of a positive number is the number itself.
The absolute value of a negative number is its opposite.

Examples: The absolute value of -9 is 9.
The absolute value of 7 is 7.
The absolute value of -132 is 132.
The absolute value of 1,378 is 1,378.
The absolute value of -1,378 is 1,378.

The child drew the numeral -7 in the sand. Then he drew the letter 'A' on one side and the letter 'V' on the other side: A-7V. "That stands for the absolute value of -7! But it looks confusing," he said. The child erased part of the A and part of the V so that his drawing looked like this: /-7/. "That looks better," he said. "/-7/ stands for the absolute value of negative 7, which is positive 7. /-8/ means the absolute value of negative eight, which is positive 8."

"We get the picture!" Negative Number grumbled. "And so on and so on."

"This is interesting," Al said, copying the numbers onto a scrap of paper. He didn't have time to draw the picture carefully, so his sketch looked like this:

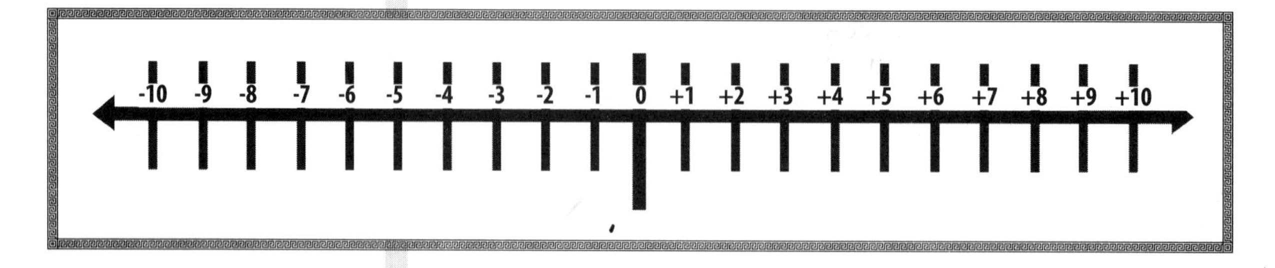

Al labeled his drawing "The Number Line."

"So far, this is what we can take to the king," Gebra said as she wrote on a scrap of paper.

1. Whole number: any of the numbers 0, 1, 2, 3, and so on
2. Mean: The arithmetic mean, often called the average or simply the mean, is the sum of the values divided by the total number of values.

Examples: The mean of 5, 7, and 9 is 7 (5 + 7 + 9 = 21; 21 ÷ 3 = 7).
The mean of 1, 57, 100, and 2 is 40 (1 + 57 + 100 + 2 = 160; 160 ÷ 4 = 40).

3. Positive numbers: Numbers that are greater than zero are positive.
4. Negative numbers: Numbers that are less than zero are negative.
5. Integers: Whole numbers and their opposites are integers.
6. Absolute value: The absolute value of a positive number is the number itself. The absolute value of a negative number is its opposite. A number and its opposite are an equal distance from zero.

Examples: The absolute value of -9 is 9.
The absolute value of 7 is 7.
The absolute value of -132 is 132.
The absolute value of 1,378 is 1,378.
The absolute value of -1,378 is 1,378.

By the time Gebra finished her list, all the integers were awake. Al and Gebra were given a hero's farewell, whereupon they started off for the Second Kingdom.

Between the Kingdoms: Axioms

The Second Kingdom

Adding Positive and Negative Numbers

"Why are you crying?" Gebra asked the king in the Second Kingdom.

"It's my daughter," said the king, sobbing as he spoke. "She keeps growing taller and taller, and then suddenly she shrinks. Can you imagine how difficult it is to keep her in properly fitting designer clothes?"

"What is your daughter's name?" Al asked, patting the king's shoulder.

"Her name is Alice—Alice Adding. She's in her play-castle now. Follow me. I'll show you."

Al and Gebra watched at a distance as Alice played with her toy knights in her play-castle. She was, at the time, three feet tall—a normal height for a child her age. On a table nearby was a bowl filled with berries. Some of the berries were black; others were white.

Alice picked up nine black berries and seven white ones and put them on a plate.

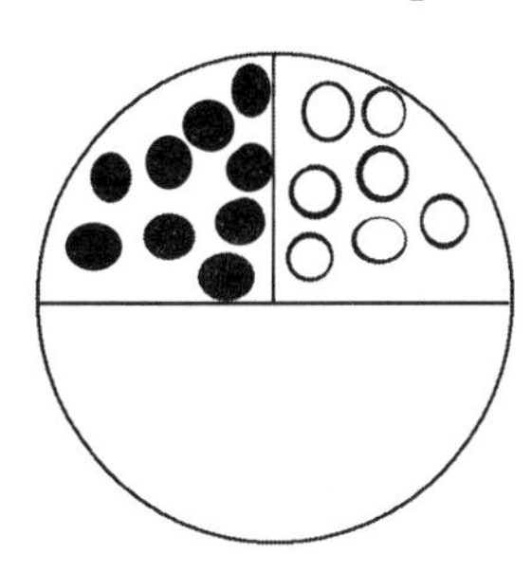

Then she added them together.

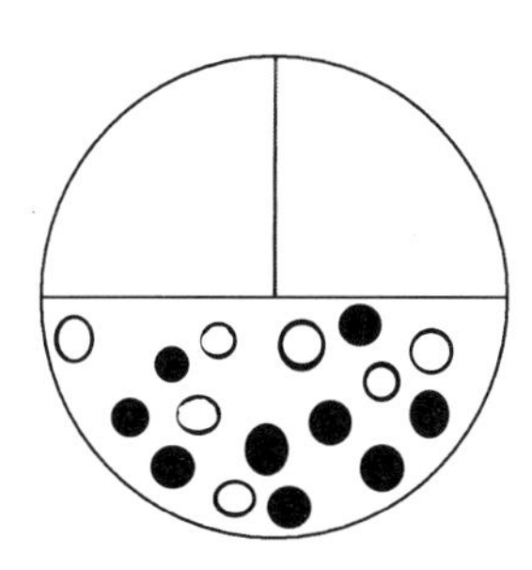

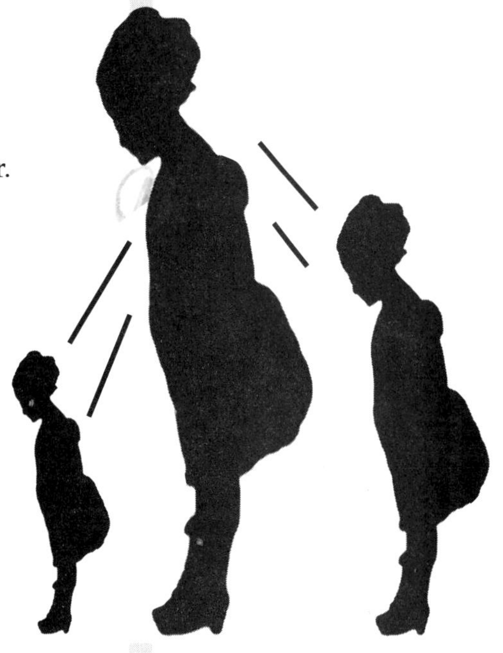

Finally she popped them all into her mouth. Alice immediately grew nine feet taller, then shrunk seven feet.

"Wow," Al said. "Did you see that? She grew, then shrunk, and now she's two feet taller than she was a minute ago." The king's sobs could be heard from the hallway.

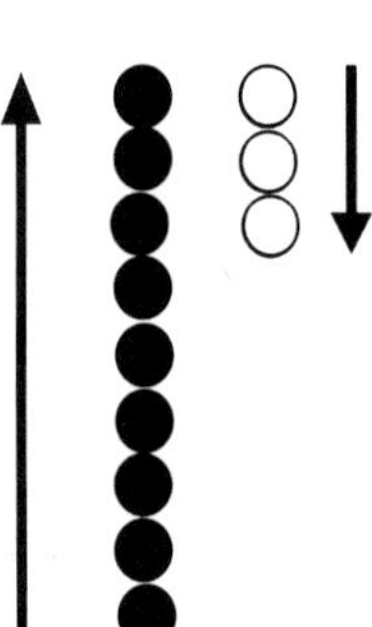

In their amazement Al and Gebra absentmindedly reached into the bowl of berries.

In one gulp Al swallowed nine black berries and three white ones. Immediately he grew nine feet taller, and then shrunk three feet. He was then six feet taller than he had been only minutes before.

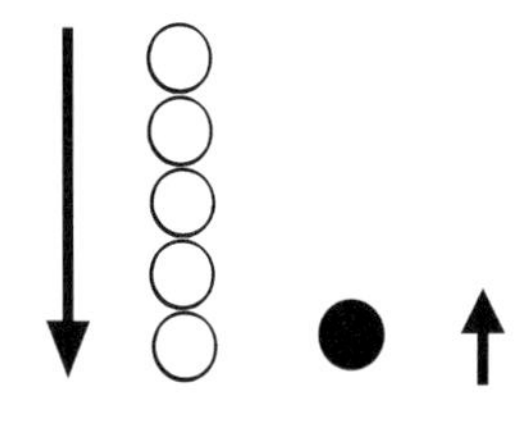

Gebra picked up five white berries and one black berry and swallowed them all at once. She immediately shrunk five feet to a height of zero, and then grew to one foot tall.

"Gebra, where are you?" Al asked, bending over to keep from hitting his head on the ceiling.

"I'm down here!" Gebra responded.

"Where?" Al took a step in the direction of Gebra's voice.

"Look out!" Gebra's tiny voice could barely be heard. Al's foot missed her by inches, and she ducked underneath a table.

"Gebra! I'm sorry," Al apologized for almost stepping on her, then picked her up and put her on the table. "What's happening?" he asked.

"All I know is that I ate five white berries and one black berry," Gebra shouted loudly for Al to hear. "Suddenly I shrunk five feet and then grew one foot."

"And I ate nine black berries and three white ones," Al said. "I grew nine feet, and then shrunk three. That's it," he reasoned. "It must be the berries that are causing us to grow and to shrink."

Replied Gebra: "Each black berry caused us to grow one foot in a positive direction, and each white berry caused us to shrink one foot in a negative direction. The black berries are positive, and the white berries are negative."

"I ate (+9) + (-3) = (+6). I grew six feet taller!" Al said. "I need to eat six negative berries to become my normal height again." He ate the six white berries hurriedly.

"And I ate (+1) + (-5) = -4. I shrunk four feet in a negative direction!" Gebra yelled. I need to eat four positive berries to become my normal height again," she said as she ate four black berries.

"So if we eat more positive berries than negative berries, we grow taller, and if we eat more negative berries than positive berries, we shrink," Al said.

"And this is what happened to Alice!" Gebra exclaimed. "I noticed that she ate nine positive berries and seven negative ones. The nine positive berries caused her to grow nine feet, and the seven negative ones caused her to shrink seven feet.

(+9) + (-7) = (+2)

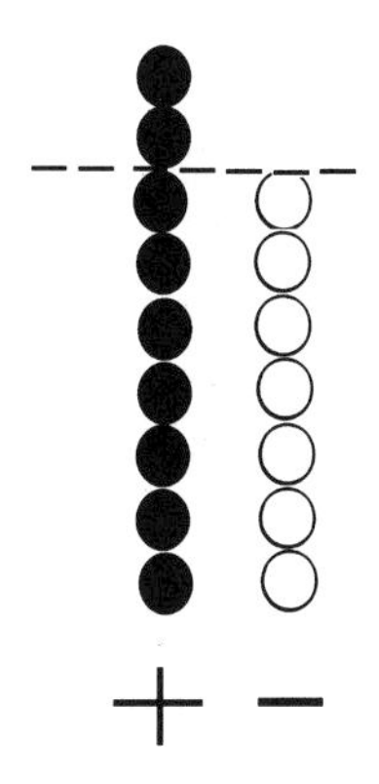

"Alice is now two feet taller than she was before she ate the berries," concluded Gebra.

Adding Two Integers: If one is positive and the other negative, find the difference of their absolute values. The result has the same sign as the addend having the greater absolute value.

Examples:

(+2) + (-3) = (-1) Three is 1 greater than 2; the largest addend, -3, is negative.
(+5) + (-13) = (-8) Thirteen is 8 greater than 5; the largest addend, -13, is negative.
(-2) + (+6) = (+4) Six is 4 greater than 2; the largest addend, 6, is positive.
(-9) + (+8) = (-1) Nine is 1 greater than 8; the largest addend, -9, is negative.

Before Al and Gebra could move, Alice Adding had reached into the bowl of berries with both hands. She had three positive berries in one hand and two positive berries in the other hand. She ate them all in one gulp.

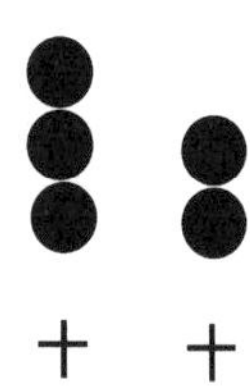

"She ate only positive berries this time. Positive three plus positive two equals positive five," Gebra said. "She will grow five feet taller."

Adding Two Integers: If both are positive, add them as you always have. The sum is positive.

Al removed the bowl of berries and ran out of the way before Alice could step on him, as she was now 10 feet tall. "Here," he said gently, holding five negative berries out to her in his right hand and two more in his left hand. Alice ate the seven negative berries hungrily.

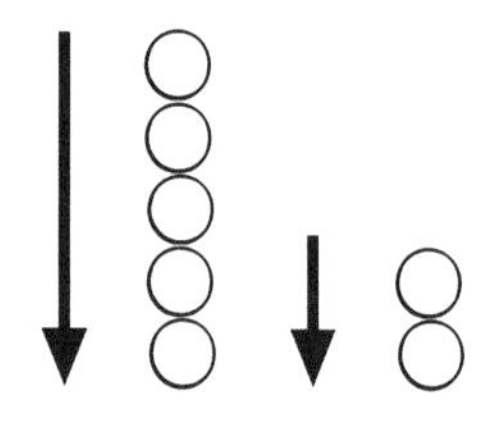

"She ate seven negative berries. I predict that she'll shrink seven feet," Al whispered to Gebra. "Then she'll be her normal height of three feet tall."

Adding Two Integers: If both are negative, add their absolute values. The sum is negative.

Examples:

$(-10) + (-7) = (-17)$

$(-1) + (-3) = (-4)$

$(-223) + (-124) = (-347)$

While Alice was shrinking, Al and Gebra took the bowl of berries away and explained to the king all that had happened. "We'll give this note to you as a reminder, just in case Alice Adding happens to find and eat more berries," Gebra said to the king.

For Alice Adding

(+) + (+) = (+)	**Example:**	(+2) + (+3) = (+5)
(-) + (-) = (-)	**Example:**	(-2) + (-3) = (-5)

(+) + (-) = **Find the difference of the absolute values; use the sign of the largest addend.**

Examples:	(+5) + (-3) = (+2)
	(-5) + (+3) = (-2)

As Al and Gebra were walking away from the play-castle, they heard a small voice. "Over here," it said.

"Where?" Al asked. "We can't see you."

"That's the problem. This morning I was eating some berries and suddenly I disappeared."

"How tall were you before eating the berries?" Al asked.

"Six feet tall."

"How many berries did you eat?" Gebra kept probing.

"Seven in all," the voice answered.

"Just what we thought," Al said as he turned around and walked back to the bowl that the king held in his hand. He selected four positive berries with one hand and three with the other.

"Here, eat these," Al said when he returned. He laid the seven berries on a nearby table, not knowing exactly where the invisible person was standing.

"Why?" asked the voice.

"Because each negative berry that you ate this morning caused you to shrink one foot. You shrunk seven feet in all," Gebra explained.

"But I was only six feet tall. How could I shrink seven feet?"

"Positive six (+6) plus negative seven (-7) equals negative one (-1). You are now negative one foot tall," Al drew a diagram as he explained.

(+6) + (-7) = (-1)

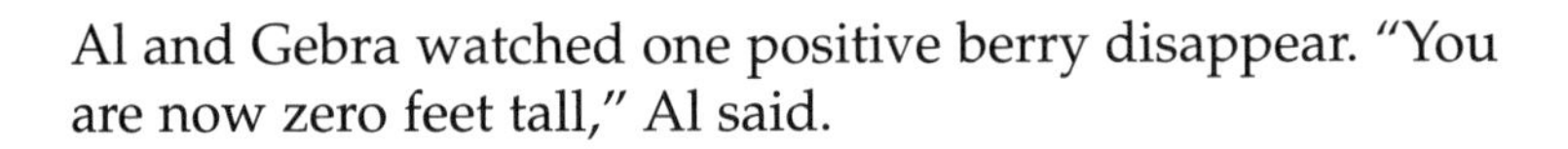

Al and Gebra watched one positive berry disappear. "You are now zero feet tall," Al said.

A second positive berry disappeared. Suddenly a one-foot-tall man appeared. The tiny man ate a third berry and was two feet tall, a fourth berry and he was three feet tall, a fifth berry and he was four feet tall, a sixth berry and he was five feet tall, and a seventh berry and he was six feet tall.

"Thank you so much." The tall man kissed Gebra's hand before leaping across the courtyard, thrilled to be his normal size again.

As Al and Gebra left the Second Kingdom, they saw children skipping rope and heard them singing this song:

Alice eats grow berries, Alice gets taller.
Alice eats shrink berries, Alice gets smaller.

She ate three grow berries, then five more.
She's eight feet taller. Don't grow any more!

She ate five shrink berries, and then she ate three.
Now she's as normal as she can be.

If she eats five grow berries, then three that make her shrink,
She'll be two feet taller than you think!

"Our adventure with Alice Adding gave us three more facts to take to the king," Al said as he quickly added notes to his scrap of paper.

Adding Two Integers

1. **If one is positive and the other negative, find the difference of their absolute values. The result has the same sign as the addend having the greater absolute value.**

   Examples:

   (+2) + (-3) = (-1) Three is 1 more than 2; the largest addend, -3, is negative.
   (+5) + (-13) = (-8) Thirteen is 8 more than 5; the largest addend, -13, is negative.
   (-2) + (+6) = (+4) Six is 4 more than 2; the largest addend, 6, is positive.
   (-9) + (8) = (-1) Nine is 1 more than 8; the largest addend, -9, is negative.

2. **If both are negative, add their absolute values. The sum is negative.**
3. **If both are positive, add them as you always have. The sum is positive.**

"Things are beginning to add up now," Gebra said with a sly smile as they left the second kingdom.

"Very funny," Al answered, shaking his head and grimacing good-naturedly at Gebra's bad joke.

Between the Kingdoms: Theorems

Theorems are statements about real numbers that can be proven to be true.

Between the Kingdoms: Variables

A variable is a symbol that is used to represent one or more numbers.

The Third Kingdom
Subtracting Positive and.Negative Numbers

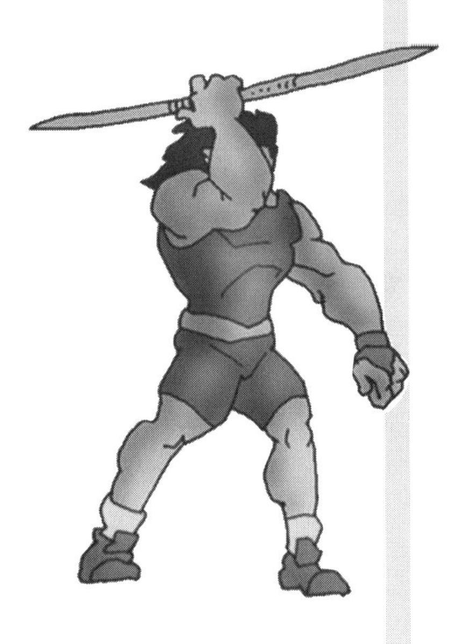

The Third Kingdom was filled with athletes. They were all stretching, lifting weights, and running, as if they were getting in shape for a major sports event.

"What's happening?" Al asked a young man who was practicing his sport.

"We're not sure," the man answered, beads of sweat standing out on his forehead. "We've been practicing for a sports event for years, but it never happens."

Al and Gebra looked at one another. "Strange," Gebra whispered. "Who's in charge here?" she asked the man.

"The queen, of course. She's in her chamber, as usual." The man nodded toward a half-open wooden door as he talked.

Neither the queen nor her court, gathered around a huge drawing table, heard Al and Gebra's knock on the door. The men and women argued as they marked on papers spread across the table.

"Excuse me," Gebra called out three times, finally shouting the third time before she got their attention. At last all faces were looking in her direction. "We're interested in hearing about the games that your sports stars will be playing."

"We don't know yet," one member of the royal court answered. "We don't know any games to play."

"Can you help us?" The queen held a piece of chalk toward Al and Gebra. When Al took the chalk, the queen and her entire court walked away. "Be ready by sunrise," the queen said over her shoulder as she left the chamber.

"What will we do?" Al asked Gebra when they were alone.

"Let's take another look at your number line," Gebra said. "Maybe it will give us an idea."

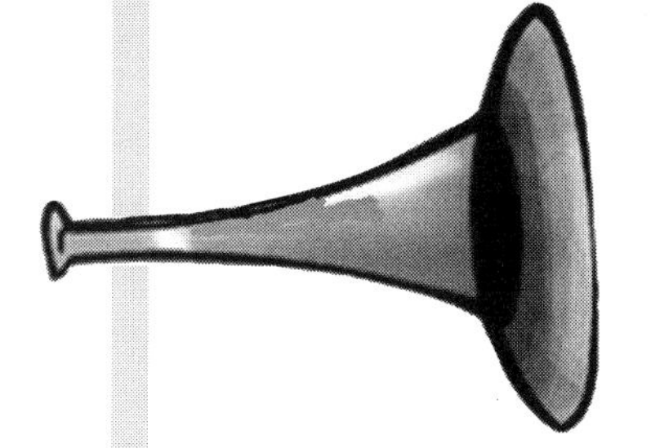

All night long Al and Gebra painted lines and discussed how the game should be scored. Just as the sun was rising, the caller blew the morning horn and all the athletes gathered on the field.

"This game is called Subtraction Reaction," Al announced through a megaphone. "Your team begins the game with a negative score. Your goal is to subtract negative points."

"This is your playing field," he continued, pointing toward a small field painted with white lines. "A heavy, weighted ball has been placed on the negative-14 yard line. Your team will have seven chances to kick the ball out of the negative side, past the zero yard line, and onto the positive side of the field."

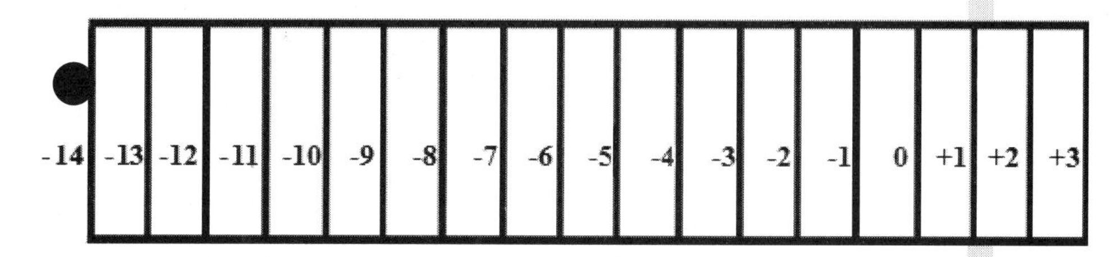

"This game is all about subtracting negative points," continued Gebra. "Your score will depend on the number of negative points that you take away from your current score of negative 14."

"But after your last kick, the opposing team will have one chance to subtract any positive points that you might have earned," Al added.

The caller once again blew the horn and the game began. The first kicker kicked the ball two yards.

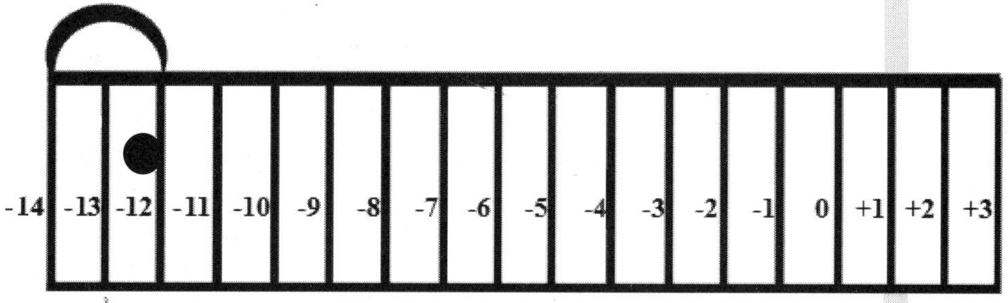

Al announced the play while the crowd cheered. "The player kicked away two negative points, landing on the negative-12 yard line. Negative 14 minus negative two equals negative 12: $(-14) - (-2) = (-12)$. The new score is negative 12 (-12)!" Al stood up with excitement.

A cheerleader led the spectators in a cheer:

To subtract a negative two
I can tell you what to do:
Change the minus to a plus;
Then we add two points for us!
Yea!

"Taking away negative numbers makes sense," a teenager who was sitting nearby said. "It's like zits. They're definitely negative. If I have seven zits and make two of them go away with some seaweed ointment, then I have taken away two negative things from seven negative things. I only have five negative things left: $(-7) - (-2) = (-5)$."

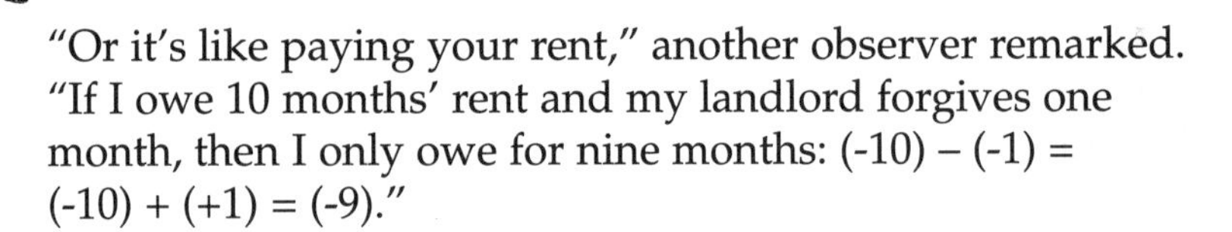

"Or it's like paying your rent," another observer remarked. "If I owe 10 months' rent and my landlord forgives one month, then I only owe for nine months: $(-10) - (-1) = (-10) + (+1) = (-9)$."

The second player kicked the ball three yards, taking away three more negative points.

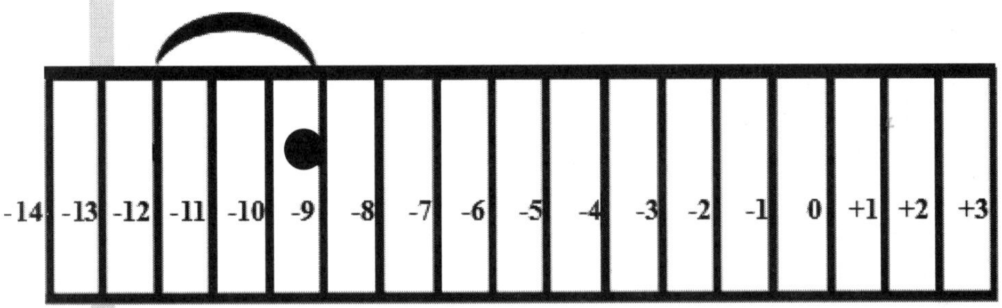

"The ball was kicked three more yards, landing on the negative-9 yard line," Gebra spoke into the megaphone. "The home team has taken away three more of its negative points. Negative 12 minus negative 3 equals negative 9: $(-12) - (-3) = (-9)$. The new score is negative nine (-9)."

The cheerleaders led the crowd in a new cheer:

To subtract a negative 3—two for you and one for me,
Change the minus to a plus. Then we add three
points for us!

"So (-12) – (-3) is the same as (-12) + (+3)!" an observer shared her new insight. "Just like the cheerleaders are saying, change the negative number to a positive, then add."

Before everyone could finish talking, the third player was ready for his kick. "No! The other way!" everyone shouted. "You're kicking in the wrong direction! You're subtracting **positive** points. You should be subtracting **negative** points!"

But it was too late. The player kicked the ball two yards in the wrong direction, farther into the negative side of the field. He subtracted two positive points from his team's score.

"Subtracting positive points is the same as adding negative points!" an angry viewer shouted.

Al announced the play. "Two positive points were subtracted from the home team's score. Or we could say that two negative points were added. The ball was at the negative-9 yard line. Now the score is negative 11. To subtract positive two, change the positive to a negative sign and add."

(-9) – (+2) = (-11) is the same as (-9) + (-2) = (-11). "This is a game of **subtracting** negative points, not adding them!" the crowd roared.

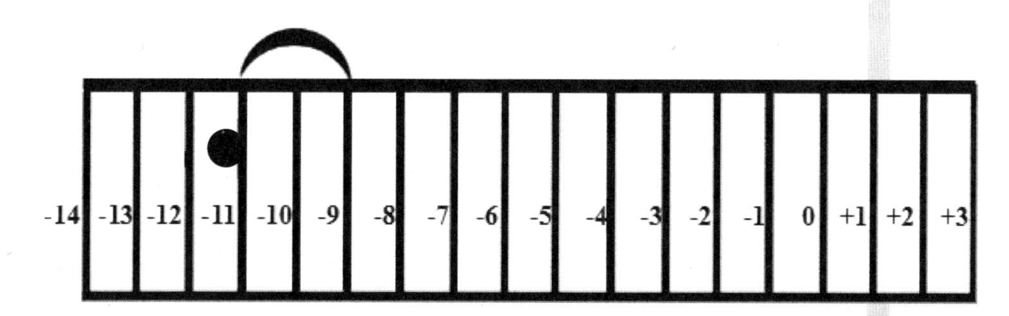

"It's now time for the fourth player," Al continued as the next kicker walked up to the ball. The crowd gasped as he sent the heavy ball flying across the field. One, two, three, four, five yards.

"This is unbelievable," Gebra shouted into the megaphone. "The ball was at negative 11. The player kicked it five yards, taking away five negative points. (-11) – (-5) = (-6) is the same as (-11) + (+5), which equals (-6)."

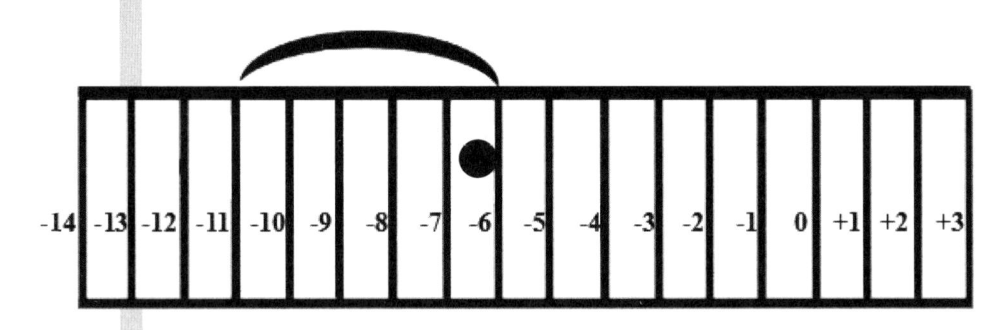

The crowd went wild as the cheerleaders shouted:

To subtract a minus 5, sit up straight and look alive.
Change the minus to a plus; then we add five points for us.

"The score is negative 6, and the home team still has three more kicks!" Al shouted the good news as the next player walked up to the ball. The crowd sat breathlessly as she kicked the ball four more yards.

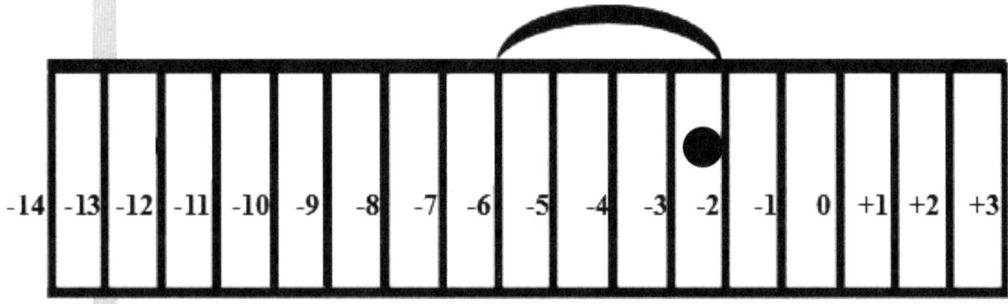

The cheerleaders shouted:

To subtract a negative 4, don't go running out the door.
Change the minus to a plus; then we add four points
for us.

"The score was negative 6. The player kicked away four negative points. Now the score is negative 2," Al shouted into the megaphone. "(-6) – (-4) is the same as
(-6) + (+4) = (-2)."

The next player kicked the ball two more yards, landing it directly on the zero yard line.

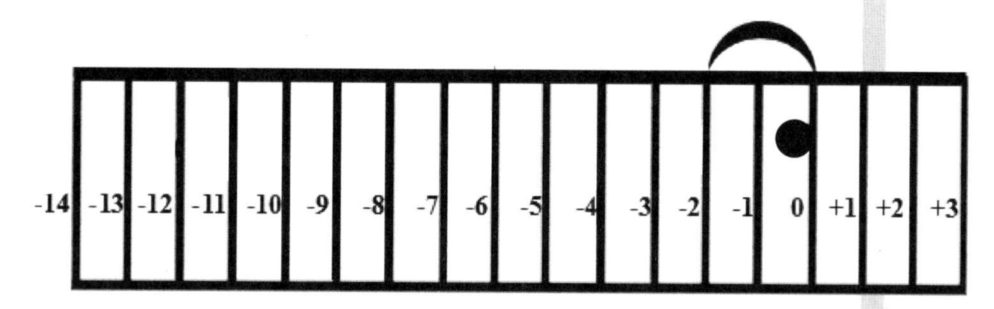

"Negative 2 minus negative 2 equals zero," Al stood up as he shouted the score, "and the home team still has one more kick remaining. Here he goes!"

The final player kicked the ball three yards onto the positive side of the field.

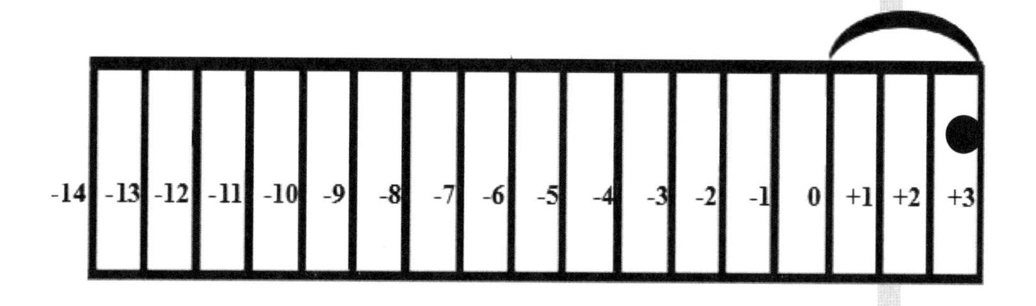

"The final player has subtracted three more negative points. The ball is now three yards in the positive direction:
0 – (-3) = 0 + (+3) = (+3). The new score is positive 3!"

The cheerleaders burst into song:

To subtract a negative number
Listen now! No time to slumber!
Change the minus to a plus,
Then we add. How 'bout us?

"Don't forget!" Gebra reminded the crowd. "The opposing team now has one chance to kick the ball back in the negative direction, adding negative points. Let's see what happens."

The spectators fell silent as the largest player on the opposing team walked up to the ball. She swung her leg backward as far as she possibly could, then kicked with all her strength. But she kicked the ball on the underside, sending it almost straight up into the air. It fell downward sharply, landing only one yard away.

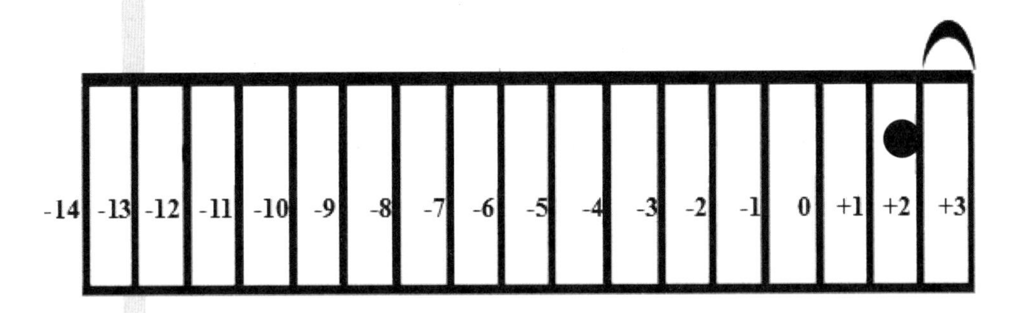

"The ball was kicked one yard by the opposing team," Gebra shouted. "The final score is positive 2: (+3) – (+1) = (+3) + (-1) = (+2)."

While everyone in the kingdom was cheering, Al and Gebra laid their megaphones down and slipped away from the stands. "They can score the rest of the games themselves. Let's get out of here so they can have their fun," Gebra whispered as the athletes raised a flag that read "The Subtraction Kingdom" over the playing field.

Al and Gebra were relieved to be on their own again as they headed toward the next kingdom. But before they were out of sight of the Subtraction Kingdom, they came upon a wide river filled with rapids. "How will we ever get across?" Al wondered aloud.

"Look behind us!" Gebra screamed, pointing toward a huge, fire-breathing dragon.

"Quick, get in here!" A princess, standing nearby in her dirty work clothes, motioned Al and Gebra toward a strange-looking contraption.

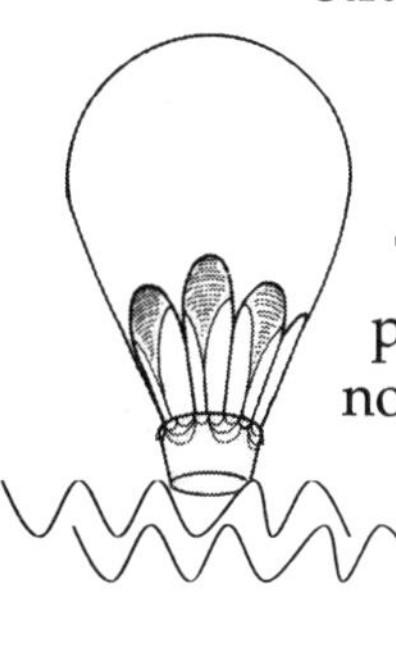

"This machine is filled with stones and balloons," said the princess. "The stones are negative. They hold the machine down. The balloons are positive. They make the machine rise. Right now it is balanced at zero, or sea level."

The princess shoved the device into the water just as the dragon reached the riverbank.

"What about you?" Al shouted to the princess.

"I'll be all right!" she answered. "This kind of dragon only eats strangers!"

Al and Gebra could feel the heat of the dragon's breath only inches from their machine as they drifted out onto the water. "That was a close one, but we're not out of trouble yet!" Al pointed in front of them as he spoke. "Look! An iceberg!"

"Our only hope is to get over it," said Gebra, trying to stay calm. "The princess said that right now we are at sea level, or zero."

"She also said the stones are negative. That means the stones make the machine go downward, in a negative direction," said Al, talking fast.

"If we take away a stone (-), the machine will rise (+)," Gebra continued. "0 – (-1) = (+1)."

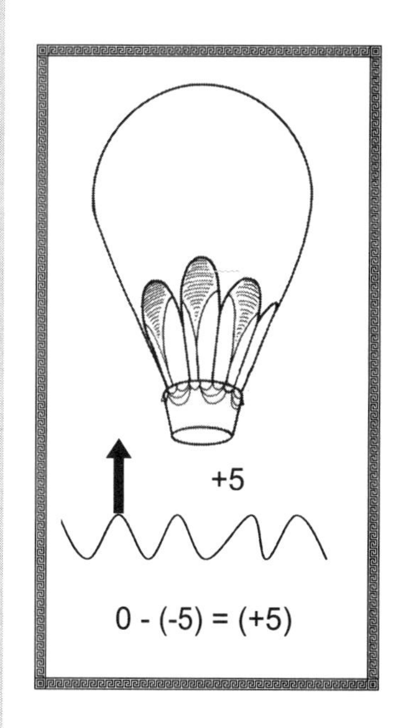

Gebra quickly threw five stones overboard. The machine suddenly lifted five feet into the air and sailed safely over the sharp peak of ice: 0 – (-5) = (+5).

"Look out!" Gebra shouted, pointing toward the flying dragon right in front of them.

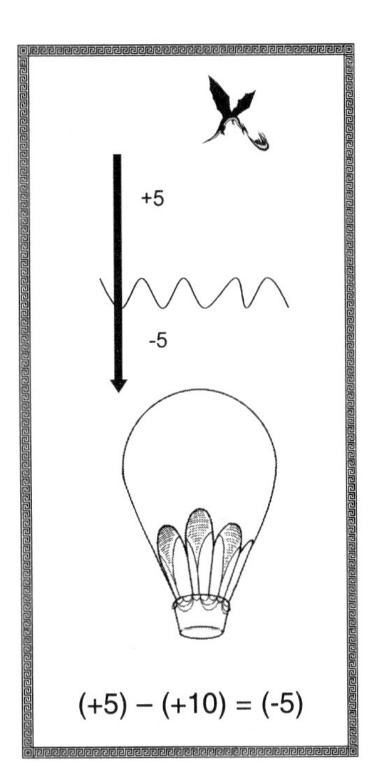

"Our only hope is to go under it," said Al, immediately throwing 10 balloons out of the machine: (+5) – (+10) = (+5) + (-10) = (-5).

The machine descended 10 feet, and they were five feet underwater.

Hoping the dragon had flown away and fearful they would drown, Gebra began throwing stones overboard. She threw five stones out, and the machine was at sea level once more: (-5) – (-5) = (-5) + (+5) = 0.

"Look at this!" Gebra said as she scribbled notes on a scrap of paper.

0 – (-5) = (+5)
0 – (-10) = (+10)
0 – (-2) = (+2)
0 – (+6) = (-6)
0 – (+4) = (-4)

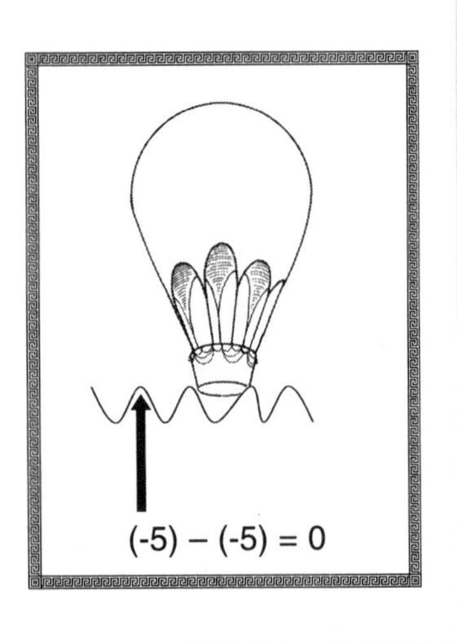

"To subtract negative 5, add positive 5;
To subtract negative 10, add positive 10;
To subtract negative 2, add positive 2;
To subtract positive 6, add negative 6;
To subtract positive 4, add negative 4."

"So," added Al, "to subtract one real number from another, simply add its opposite."

(-2) – (-3) = (-2) + (+3) = (+1)
(-2) – (+3) = (-2) + (-3) = (-5)
(+2) – (-3) = (+2) + (+3) = (+5)
(+2) – (+3) = (+2) + (-3) = (-1)

As they reached the banks of the next kingdom, Al and Gebra could hear the cheerleaders at the Subtraction Reaction game singing this song:

To subtract negative 1, we can have a little fun;
Change the minus to a plus, then we add one point for us.

To subtract negative 2, we know just what we should do;
Change the minus to a plus, then we add two points for us.

To subtract negative 3, two for you and one for me;
Change the minus to a plus, then we add three points for us.

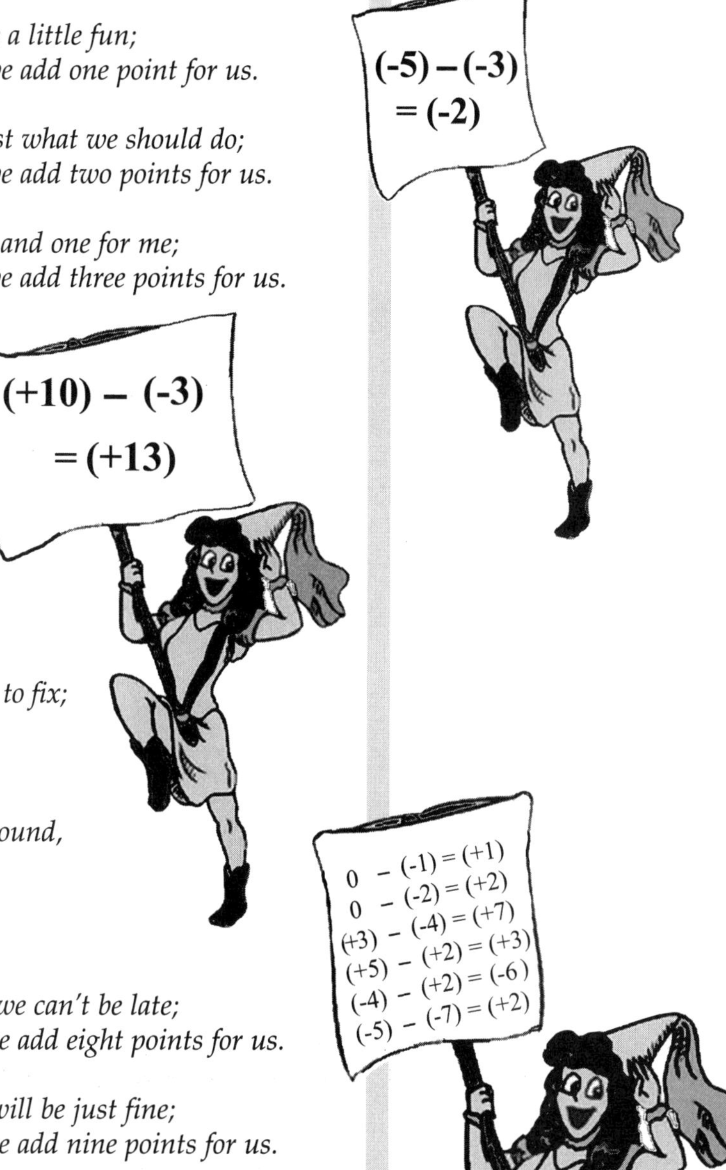

To subtract negative 4,
Don't go running out the door;
Change the minus to a plus,
Then we add four points for us.

To subtract negative 5,
Sit up straight and look alive;
Change the minus to a plus,
Then we add five points for us.

To subtract negative 6 is an easy one to fix;
Change the minus to a plus,
Then we add six points for us.

To subtract negative 7, touch the ground,
Then look toward heaven;
Change the minus to a plus,
Then we add seven points for us.

To subtract negative 8, hurry now, we can't be late;
Change the minus to a plus, then we add eight points for us.

To subtract negative 9, everything will be just fine;
Change the minus to a plus, then we add nine points for us.

To subtract negative 10, touch your toes and touch your chin;
Change the minus to a plus, then we add 10 points for us.

To subtract a negative number, listen now, no time to slumber!
Change the minus to a plus, then we add … How 'bout us?!

Between the Kingdoms: The Commutative Property

Between the Kingdoms: The Associative Property

Between the Kingdoms: Symbols of Multiplication

The Fourth Kingdom

Multiplying and Dividing Positive and Negative Numbers

"My lady," a deep voice reverberated through the air as Al and Gebra stood at the gate of the Fourth Kingdom. Suddenly a man with dark-gray eyes appeared out of nowhere. He stood perfectly still, only inches in front of Gebra, holding a rose in one hand and a thorn in the other.

"Life is like a garden," the man whispered.
"Roses are positive (+). Thorns are negative (-).
Planting is positive (+). Killing is negative (-)."

Gebra nodded.

"Planting roses is positive," the man said slowly, handing Gebra a rose as he spoke. Then he wrote in the sand: (+) (+) = (+).

"Killing roses is negative." The man took the rose away, crushed it in his fist, then wrote (-) (+) = (-).

"Planting thorns is negative," the man continued, handing Gebra a thorn. It pricked her finger, filling her palm with blood, but she did not look away. The man wrote (+) (-) = (-) in the sand.

"Killing thorns is positive," the man said as he wrote (-) (-) = (+) in the sand. He took the thorn from Gebra's fingers, then squeezed a scrap of paper into her hand and whispered, "Multiply goodness." Finally he disappeared.

$(+)\ (+) = (+)$
$(+)\ (-) = (-)$
$(-)\ (+) = (-)$
$(-)\ (-) = (+)$

"Who was that?" Gebra gasped when she caught her breath.

"I have no idea. What's on the scrap of paper?" Al asked.

Gebra smoothed the crumpled, blood-soaked wad. "It's a chart," she said. "It contains the same symbols that the mysterious man wrote in the sand."

"The man's final words were 'multiply goodness,'" Al said, "so this chart must tell us how to multiply."

Gebra wrote the words, "How to Multiply Positive and Negative Numbers" at the top of the page.

Al added the words "roses," "thorns," "planting," and "killing" to the chart, beside the appropriate symbols.

How to Multiply Positive and Negative Numbers

$(+)\ (+) = (+)$ **Planting roses is positive.**
$(+)\ (-) = (-)$ **Planting thorns is negative.**
$(-)\ (+) = (-)$ **Killing roses is negative.**
$(-)\ (-) = (+)$ **Killing thorns is positive.**

When he finished writing, Al tugged at Gebra's arm and said, "Let's get out of here."

"My guess is that we'll need to know how to multiply positive and negative numbers in the Fourth Kingdom," Gebra said as she folded the scrap of paper and tucked it beneath her wristband.

Instantly the drawbridge fell at their feet and, without hesitation, Al and Gebra crossed the wooden beams into the Fourth Kingdom. Inside the fortress walls, people stood in small groups, whispering. Everyone looked worried. In the center of the courtyard, a beautiful princess stood alone.

"You look troubled, Your Majesty. What's wrong?" Al asked.

"Four bands of knights wish to join our kingdom," the princess replied. "Some have performed good deeds. Others, evil. We need good warriors, but we don't know how much to pay them. And the evil ones must pay appropriately for their wrongdoing."

Al leaned over the fortress wall to look at the bands of knights. He saw huge thorns and brilliantly colored roses climbing the gray rocks. "I think we can help," he said. Everyone in the courtyard fell silent. "Invite a leader from each band to enter, then instruct the leaders to bear gifts that represent the deeds of their knights."

The invitation was announced from the watchtower, the drawbridge was lowered, and the princess returned to her throne. Guards in the towers stretched their bows, ready to defend their kingdom.

The first knight rode a black steed. His armor was totally white, except for three red roses and 72 red marks painted on his shield. He bowed a deep bow and laid the shield at the princess's feet. "Your Majesty," he began, "there are 72 knights in my band, and each knight has performed three acts of bravery."

"Performing acts of bravery is like planting (+) flowers (+)," Al whispered to the princess. "Seventy-two knights each performed three acts of bravery: (+72) (+3) = (+216). This band should be welcomed into your kingdom, and their pay should be 216 coins."

The second knight rode a white horse. Her armor was shiny black, with four silver thorns painted in the center of her white shield. Each thorn was broken in half. Twenty-eight marks formed a line across the top of her shield. "Your Majesty," she said, "there are 28 knights in my band. Each knight has stopped four others from committing evil deeds."

"Stopping acts of treachery is like killing (-) thorns (-)," Gebra said to the princess. "Twenty-eight knights each stopped four acts of treachery: (-28) (-4) = (+112). This band should be welcomed into your kingdom, and their pay should be 112 coins."

The third knight rode a dappled, gray-and-white mare. His armor was a velvety red, except for two crushed, white roses painted in the center of his black shield. Fifty white marks formed a line across the top of his shield. "Your Majesty," he said, "there are 50 knights in my band. Much to my regret, each knight has interfered with two acts of bravery."

"Stopping acts of bravery is like killing (-) flowers (+)," Al said to the princess. "Fifty knights each stopped two acts of bravery: (-50) (+2) = (-100). These knights should pay one hundred coins before being allowed to join your kingdom."

The fourth knight rode a red stallion with a white mane and tail. Her armor was emerald green, except for eight perfectly formed thorns painted on her white shield. Twelve marks formed a line across the top of her shield. "Your Majesty," she said, "there are 12 knights in my band. Much to my regret, each knight has committed eight acts of treachery."

"Committing acts of treachery is like planting (+) thorns (-)," Gebra said to the princess. "Twelve knights each committed eight acts of treachery: (+12) (-8) = (-96). This band must pay 96 coins before they will be worthy of joining your kingdom."

Early the next morning the princess sent for Al and Gebra. "Thanks to you, ours is the most powerful kingdom in the world," she said, clasping Al's and Gebra's hands. "Here is a token of our appreciation," she added as the four lead knights walked forward, bearing two beautiful shields for Al's and Gebra's horses. Each shield was decorated with one rose and one broken thorn. Al and Gebra thanked them for the gifts and departed for the Fifth Kingdom.

Neither Al nor Gebra spoke for hours as they rode toward the Fifth Kingdom; their heads were filled with events from their journey. Al finally broke the silence. "I noticed on the diagram that when we multiply like signs, either (+) (+) or (-) (-), the product is positive. Unlike signs, such as (+) (-), have a negative product," he said.

"That's one way to remember how to multiply signed numbers," Gebra said. "We can remember how to multiply either by thinking about roses and thorns—or by remembering that like signs produce a positive, and unlike signs produce a negative."

As they rode along, Gebra sang a song.

Like signs produce a positive; unlike signs do not.
If unlike signs are all you have, a negative's all you've got!

"I like your song, but your grammar is terrible!" Al teased, then pointed to a field in front of them. "Look at the children working in that garden," he said. "I've heard that the children who work the gardens are paid like this:

When they plant (+) a rose (+) they are paid (+) three coins: (+) (+) = (+).
When they kill (-) a rose (+) they are penalized (-) three coins: (-) (+) = (-).
When they kill (-) a thorn (-) they are paid (+) three coins: (-) (-) = (+).
When they plant (+) a thorn (-) they are penalized (-) three coins: (+) (-) = (-).

"From the looks of their garden, they haven't made much money today," Al said, smiling.

"They killed (-3) four thorns (-4):
(-4) (-3) = (+12).

"But they accidentally planted (+3) two thorns (-2):
(-2) (+3) = (-6).

"And they planted (+3) eight roses (+8):
(+8) (+3) = (+24).

"Oh, my, they killed (-3) four roses (+4):
(+4) (-3) = (-12).

"So far they earned 18 coins altogether. That's not too bad."

"I think we're ready for the Fifth Kingdom," Al and Gebra both said at once. As they spurred their horses into action, a breeze suddenly filled the air, rustling through the leaves of the trees. "Well done," the breeze seemed to be saying. "You're following my directions for multiplying signed numbers perfectly. Remember:

When good things (+) arrive (+), this is good (+),
When good things (+) leave (-), this is bad (-),
When bad things (-) arrive (+), this is bad (-),
When bad things (-) leave, (-), this is good.

"Now remember this: 'The rules you use when you multiply are the same ones you will use when you divide.'"

"Do you get the feeling someone is following us?" Gebra asked.

"It must be our imaginations," Al said.

Between the Kingdoms: The Distributive Property

The Fifth Kingdom
Fractions

The Fifth Kingdom, called the Kingdom of Parts, was filled with children, and they were all crying. "What in the world is wrong?" Gebra asked one of them.

"We have no names," one child explained.

"That's right," another one added. "We're not big enough to be integers, so we don't have any names at all."

"Well, let's think of something," Al suggested as he dismounted his horse and stood beside a child. "Since it would take two of you to be as tall as one of me, I will name you 'One-Half,'" he said. Then he moved on to the next child.

"It would take three of you to be as tall as one of me, so I will name you 'One-Third,'" he said, and then continued naming the rest of the children one at a time.

"It would take four of you to be as tall as one of me, so I will name you 'One-Fourth.'"

"It would take five of you to be as tall as one of me, so I will name you 'One-Fifth.'"

"It would take six of you to be as tall as one of me, so I will name you 'One-Sixth.'"

"It would take seven of you to be as tall as one of me, so I will name you 'One-Seventh.'"

"It would take eight of you to be as tall as one of me, so I will name you 'One-Eighth.'"

"It would take nine of you to be as tall as one of me, so I will name you 'One-Ninth.'"

"It would take ten of you to be as tall as one of me, so I will name you 'One-Tenth.'"

"Now you all have names," said Gebra, "and because you live in the Kingdom of Parts, you will be called 'fractions.'"

"So when I go walking with my mother, whose name is Forty-Seven," One-Half commented, "together she and I will be Forty-Seven and One-Half."

"That's right—one integer and one fraction. The two of you will be a mixed number," Al responded. "And now that you all have names, you can join the Kingdom of Integers, and together you will be called the Kingdom of Real Numbers," he added.

"How do we fit in with adding, subtracting, multiplying, dividing, and the order of operations for integers?" One-Eighth asked. "Do we have special rules?"

"You follow the same rules as the integers," said Al in a comforting voice. "You don't need to learn any special rules."

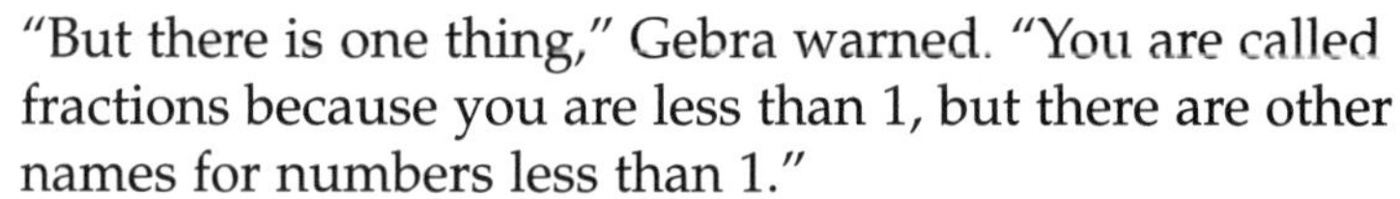

"But there is one thing," Gebra warned. "You are called fractions because you are less than 1, but there are other names for numbers less than 1."

"What other names?" several of the fractions asked at once.

"Sometimes numbers less than one are called 'decimals,'" Gebra answered.

"I don't understand," One-Tenth said.

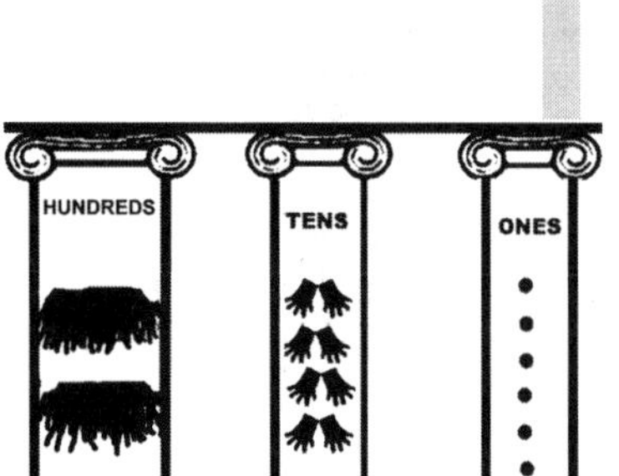

"Let me tell you about my great-great-great-great-grandmother," Gebra said. "She was a glove maker, and her name was Decimal Point. Whenever Decimal Point finished making a glove finger, she would hang it on a column she called the ONES column. When she had ten glove fingers, she would sew them together to make a pair of gloves.

"Each pair of gloves had ten fingers, so she would hang the completed pairs of gloves on a column she called the TENS column. When she finished ten pairs of gloves, she bundled them all together and hung the bundle on the HUNDREDS column because ten pairs of gloves have 100 fingers." Gebra sketched pictures in the sand as she talked.

"That makes sense," the fractions agreed.

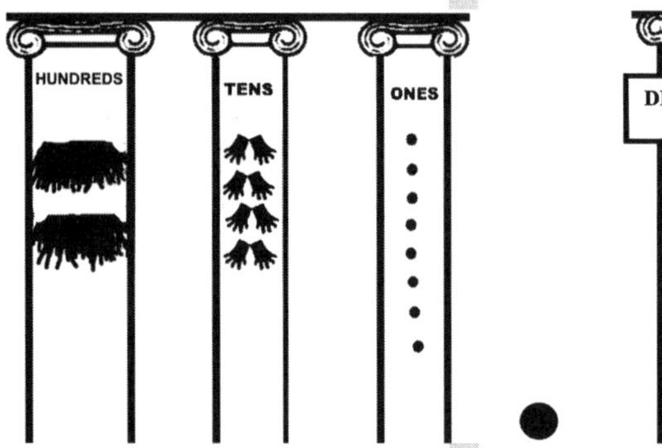

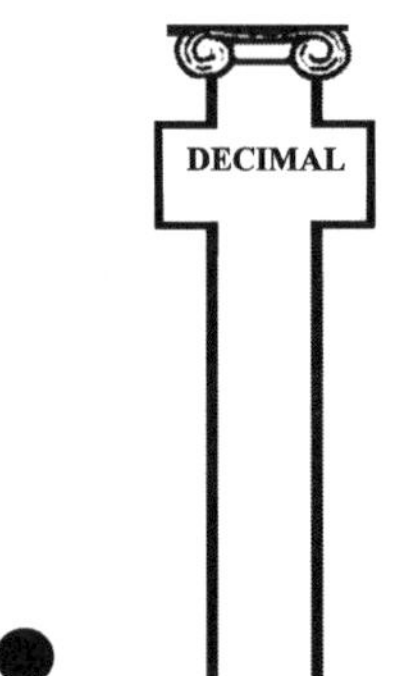

"One day Decimal Point began making a glove finger, but she didn't have time to finish it. So she picked up a huge rock, which she named after herself—Decimal Point—and she laid the rock beside the ONES column. Then she built another column to the right of the decimal point. She called that column the DECIMAL column. From that day forward, whenever she had a glove finger that she didn't have time to complete, she would hang it on the DECIMAL column."

"So now numbers less than 1 are sometimes called decimals," One-Seventh observed.

"Exactly," Al replied. "And when we're reading a number, we say 'point' when we get to the decimal point."

"One day Decimal Point completed 248 glove fingers, and three of the ten rows of another finger. She hung the partially finished glove finger on the DECIMAL column. So that day she made 248.3 (two hundred forty-eight point three) glove fingers in all," Gebra explained.

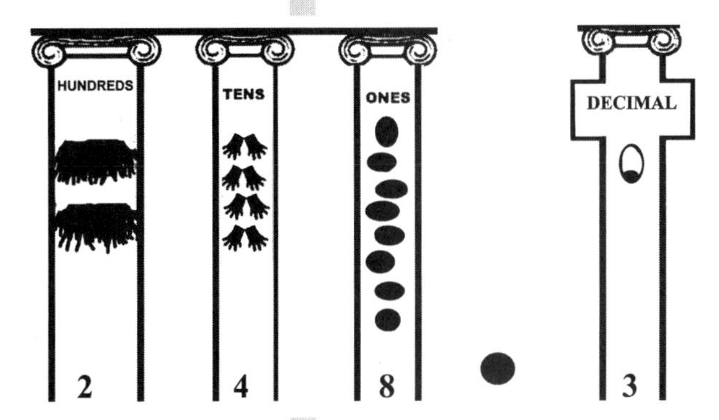

"Another day she made 125.6 (one hundred twenty-five point six) glove fingers," Gebra said.

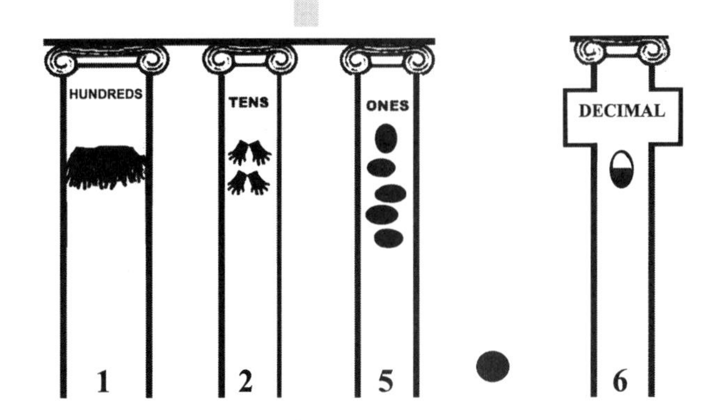

"But one day she made 104 glove fingers. She didn't start a glove finger that she didn't finish!"

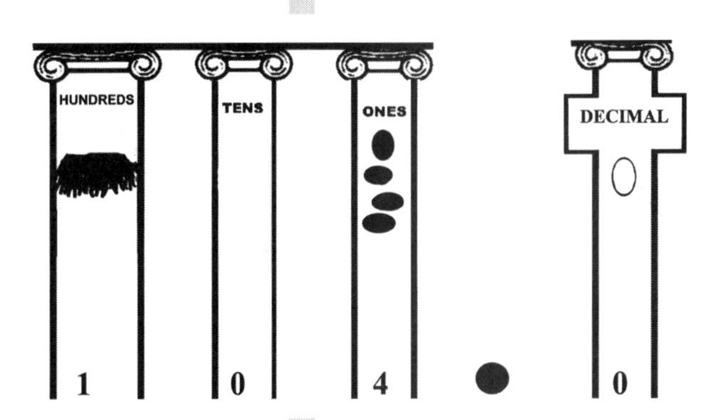

All the fractions laughed. "We think we understand," they said, nodding their heads in agreement. "Now let us show you a game we play," one of the fractions said. "We call this game 'Equivalent Fractions.'"

"Two-fourths equal one-half."

"One-fourth equals two-eighths."

"Two-fourths equal four-eighths."

"Also, two-fourths equal one-half, and four-eighths equal one-half."

"This game looks fun," Al said. "I think I'll play. One equals two-halves."

"Now that you all have names, you can return to the Kingdom of Integers," said Gebra. "Then the kingdom can be renamed the Kingdom of Real Numbers, because fractions will be there."

The fractions started running toward the gate, and Al and Gebra headed for the sixth kingdom.

Between the Kingdoms: Equations

An equation is a mathematical sentence that states that two expressions name the same number.

Between the Kingdoms: Balanced Equations

The Sixth Kingdom
Exponents

"Wow!" Al and Gebra said in unison when they saw the distant walls of the Sixth Kingdom. Above the fortress, red banners and huge EXPO signs could be seen from miles away. "They're having an expo! This should be great!"

Al and Gebra spurred their horses to a full gallop, heading straight toward the drawbridge.

"What was that?" Al sounded alarmed as he swatted at a small object that flew close to his head.

"It's a nent! Beware of the nents!" The warning came from underneath the drawbridge. "They're terrible, terrible," the voice repeated. "Beware of the nents."

"Who are you?" Gebra asked.

"Some people call me a square because I don't like excitement."

"OK, so we'll call you Square!" Al teased.

"And some people call me 'Root' because I want to get to the root of this nent problem," the voice continued.

"OK, we'll call you Square Root," Gebra decided out loud.

The voice finally emerged from under the drawbridge, hidden beneath a funny-looking box.

"That's a radical box," Al said.

"That's exactly what it's called—a radical. I'm hiding underneath it so the nents can't get to me."

"What do nents do to you?" Gebra was getting nervous now.

"Follow me; I'll show you. But keep your head low," Square Root said as he crawled up the drawbridge with the radical box on his back.

Neither Al nor Gebra was prepared for what they saw when they entered the Sixth Kingdom. For a long time they were silent. Finally Al whispered to Square Root, "Everyone looks so old!"

"It's because of the nents!" Al could see two eyes peeking out from under the radical box as Square Root spoke. "People who are bitten by a nent immediately catch a terrible disease."

Again surveying the scene before them, Gebra asked, "Does the disease make them old?"

"Exactly. If you're bitten by a nent, your age is immediately multiplied."

"Multiplied by how much?"

"By itself."

"I'm 17," Al said. "Does this mean that if I were bitten by a nent I would be … let's see … 17 times 17 years old? Would I be 289 years old?!"

"That's right," Square Root replied. "But it could be worse. The age you'll become depends on the power of the nent that bites you."

"Are some nents more powerful than others?" Al asked.

"I'm afraid so. If you were bitten by a nent that has a power of 3, you would immediately become 17^3, which means 17 X 17 X 17, or 4,913 years old!"

"Oh, my," said Gebra, who could hardly speak. "I'm 16. So if I were bitten by a nent that has a power of 4, I would become 16 to the fourth power, which means 16 X 16 X 16 X 16, or 65,536 years old."

"Look out! Here comes a nent. That one looks like a tiny little 5 flying over your head. If it bites you, you will immediately become 16 to the fifth power, or 16 X 16 X 16 X 16 X 16, which equals 1,048,576 years old. Duck!"

Al and Gebra ducked under their horses, afraid to look up.

"It's OK. The nent is gone," said Square Root.

"Why are there so many nents here in this kingdom?" asked Al.

"Because they only attack at expos. Our kingdom was planning a grand expo. The very day we put our sign up, the nents appeared."

"They must be expo-nents," Gebra said, smiling slightly at her insight.

"This problem might be more difficult to solve than the others," Al mused. "Square Root, have you ever been bitten by an expo-nent?"

"Yes, I have," Square Root answered. "But amazingly, when I crawled underneath this radical box, I returned to my original age."

"I think Square Root has already solved this problem," Gebra exclaimed.

"That's right! All we need to do is to put each person who has been bitten by a nent under Square Root's radical box. Here comes one now. How old are you?" Al asked the woman.

"I am 10,648 years old. I was bitten by a nent that had the power of 3," she answered.

"Here, come this way." Al motioned for the woman to crawl under the radical box.

Gebra programmed the radical box to find the number that, when multiplied by itself three times, equaled 10,648. Immediately the woman returned to her original age of 22.

"So 22 X 22 X 22 = 10,648," Gebra said. "But you're now your original age again," she added encouragingly.

Next a 2,500-year-old man crawled underneath the radical box. "A nent the power of 2 bit me," he said.

Al programmed the radical box to find the number that, when multiplied by itself, equaled 2,500. Immediately the man returned to his original age of 50.

"The square root of 2,500 is 50, your appropriate age," Gebra said to the man.

The man left shouting and dancing, elated to be 50 years old again.

"I was bitten by two nents," the next woman explained. "First, I was bitten by a nent that had the power of 2. Then I was bitten by another nent with the power of 3."

"$(x^2)^3$," Al said. "That's pretty old!"

Al and Gebra helped the woman to crawl under the radical box. She immediately became 20 years old again.

"Wow!" Gebra exclaimed. "If you were 20 before you were bitten by the first nent, and your age was multiplied by itself two times, you became 400 years old. 20 X 20 = 400. Then, when you were 400 years old, you were bitten by a nent that had the power of 3. You became 64,000,000 years old! 400 X 400 X 400 = 64,000,000."

A man wearing a battered black hat spoke next. "I don't remember how old I was before I was bitten by a nent that had the power of 4, but I know I was twice as old as she was," said the man, pointing to a young woman standing nearby.

"So if she was x years old, you were (2x). Then you were bitten by an expo-nent that had the power of 4. That made $(2x)^4$, which is the same as (2x) (2x) (2x) (2x), which is equal to $16(x^4)$," Al said.

"How old are you now?" Gebra asked.

After a momentary pause, the man said, "I'm now 2,560,000 years old." The man's voice was barely audible.

"So 2,560,000 = $16(x^4)$. Dividing both sides by 16, we know that 160,000 = (x^4). Twenty to the fourth power is 160,000. The lady was 20 years old. You were 2x, so you were 40," commented Gebra.

The man crawled under the radical box and immediately became 40 years old.

"Thanks to Square Root and his radical box, this problem is solved," Al said as one person after another crawled beneath the radical box and found the roots of his or her old age. Square Root watched proudly, hardly noticing as Al and Gebra mounted their horses and rode away.

Between the Kingdoms: Squares

Hi, you know me. I am an exponent. I have the power of 2.

I have the least power of all the exponents (except for the numeral 1, of course), but I can do something special. Watch this:

When I cause base numbers to be multiplied by themselves,

such as $5^2 = 5 \times 5 = 25$, or
$10^2 = 10 \times 10 = 100$, or
$8^2 = 64$,

the product is special because it can be arranged in a square. Look at this:

$2^2 = 2 \times 2 = 4$

$3^2 = 3 \times 3 = 9$

$4^2 = 4 \times 4 = 16$

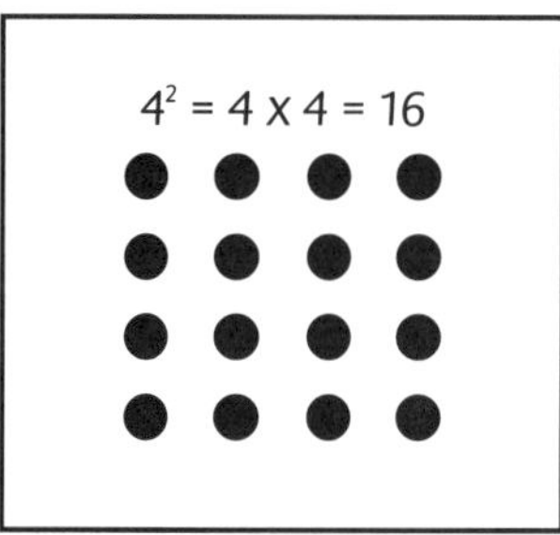

$5^2 = 5 \times 5 = 25$

$6^2 = 6 \times 6 = 36$

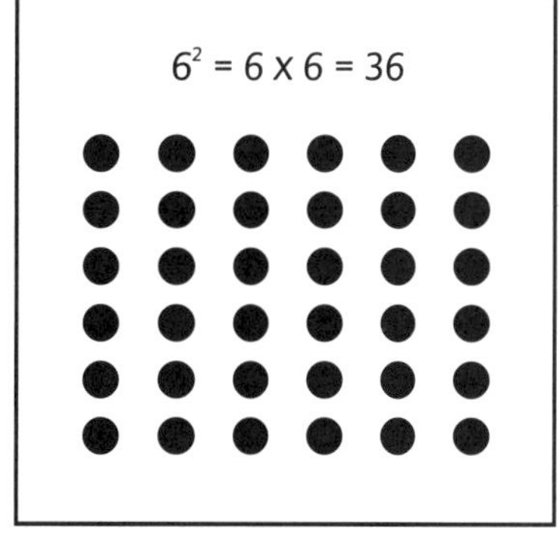

That's why they call me a square. Instead of saying "5 to the second power," people usually say "5 squared" and write 5^2. And instead of saying "8 to the second power," they usually say "8 squared," write 8^2, and so on.

Between the Kingdoms: More Squares

And now for the grand finale!

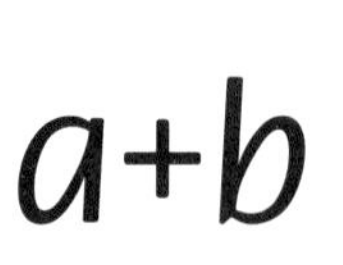

a+b
(a²+2ab+b²)

This makes sense two ways:
(a + b)(a + b) = a² + 2ab + b², or ...
a + b
a + b
ab + b²
a² + ab
a² + 2ab + b²

(a + b)(a + b) = a² + 2ab + b² is the way I've seen this done most often.
It uses the distributive property:
(a + b)(a + b) = a² + 2ab + b²

Some people remember the steps with a memory device, FOIL, which stands for First, Outside, Inside, Last.
(a + b)(a + b) = a² + ab + ab + b²
F O I L

FOIL, I like that. By the way, I need a magician's assistant! Are you interested?

Between the Kingdoms: Cubes

When I cause base numbers to be multiplied by themselves,

such as $5^3 = 5 \times 5 \times 5 = 125$, or
$10^3 = 10 \times 10 \times 10 = 1{,}000$, or
$8^3 = 8 \times 8 \times 8 = 512$

the product is special because it can be arranged in a cube. Look at this:

$(2)^3 = 2 \times 2 \times 2 = 8$

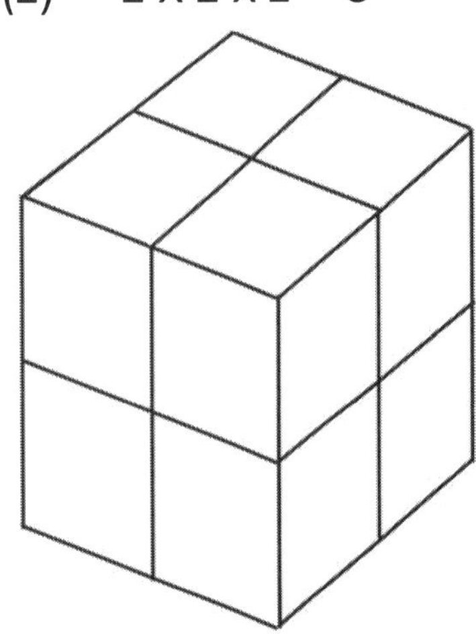

$(3)^3 = 3 \times 3 \times 3 = 27$

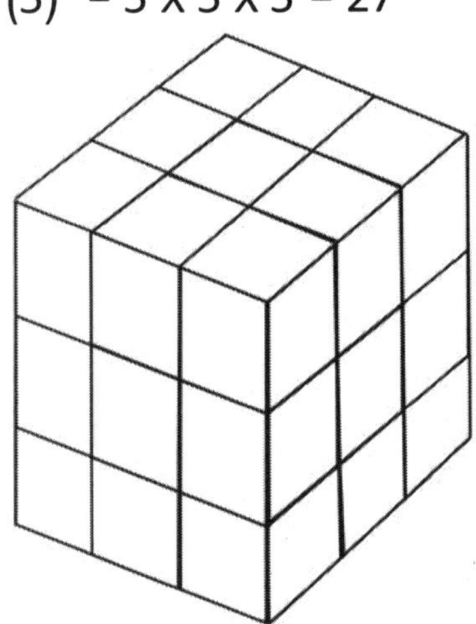

That's why they call me a cube. Instead of saying "5 to the third power," people usually say "5 cubed" and write 5^3. And instead of saying "8 to the third power," they usually say "8 cubed," write 8^3, and so on.

Now, don't you think cubes are cute?

The Seventh Kingdom

Grouping Symbols and the Order of Operations

"Ouch," Gebra said, pulling her horse to a stop. "I have a splinter in my finger."

"Let's go to the castle clinic," Al responded. "It isn't far from here."

Inside the clinic a doctor in a gray coat met them. She held a magnifying glass in her hand. "Yes, it's a splinter," she said. "There are a number of operations that we could do." The doctor handed Gebra a list:

1. Bring in fire-eating dragon to burn splinter out.
2. Pull out splinter with tweezers.
3. Attach leeches to finger to draw out infection.
4. Slit finger open with sword and remove splinter.

"Now, which operation would you like us to try first?" she asked.

"Thank you for asking, doctor," said Gebra, quickly drawing parentheses around her choice:

(2. Pull out splinter with tweezers.)

"There," Gebra said to the doctor. "I drew grouping symbols around the operation I want you to try first."

"Good. Now I know the order of operations," said the doctor, settling back in her chair as she spoke, "but there are two steps to pulling a splinter out with tweezers. I must pull the splinter out, and I must sterilize the tweezers. Which should I do first?" The doctor handed Gebra another list.

Gebra drew brackets around the words [sterilize tweezers], then she added another step. As she handed the list back to the doctor she said, "I added more grouping symbols. I want you to do the step inside the brackets first, then complete the other step inside the parentheses, then complete the step outside the parentheses."

The new order of operations looked like this:

([sterilize tweezers] + pull out splinter) + put bandage on finger

"OK, I'll do the step that's inside the parentheses first, beginning with the one that's inside the brackets," the doctor said, bending to her work.

When the splinter was removed, the doctor announced happily, "The operation is a success!" While the doctor was applying the bandage to Gebra's finger, an elderly woman came in and knocked over a pail of water. "Please excuse my dear Aunt Sally," the doctor said without looking up from her work.

"Maybe there was something we needed to learn from this experience," Al said as he and Gebra paid the doctor and left the clinic.

"Lemonade! Get your lemonade here!" two small voices shouted as Al and Gebra crossed the drawbridge into the Seventh Kingdom.

"I would love some lemonade," Al smiled at the children as he dismounted and handed them a coin. Al was thirsty, so he took a big gulp of the beverage, only to spit it back out, coughing and wiping his mouth. "This is terrible!" he gasped.

The children looked straight at Al and replied, "That's what everyone says. But we followed the recipe!"

Al took the sheet of paper that the children offered him. Still coughing, he examined the recipe.

Add $\frac{2 \times 3}{3} + (5 - [^1/_2 \times 8])^2 - 2$ teaspoons of salt

"We followed the recipe precisely!" said one child, beginning the explanation. "First we multiplied 2 times 3 to get 6. Then we added 6 plus 5 to get 11. Then we subtracted one-half to get $10^1/_2$. Then we multiplied $10^1/_2$ times 8 to get 84. Next we looked at the exponent and multiplied 84 times 84 and got 7,056. Then we subtracted 2, to get 7,054, and finally we divided 7,054 by 3 and got a little over 2,351. So we added 2,351 teaspoons of salt," said the tallest child, pointing to the recipe as she spoke.

"Could there be a problem with their order of operations?" asked Gebra.

"Gebra's right," Al said to the children. "We must solve equations in a certain order. We call this the order of operations."

"What is the order of operations?" several children asked.

Al and Gebra looked at one another. "I know we should do what is inside the parentheses first, but after that I'm not sure," Al said.

"Please excuse my dear Aunt Sally," Gebra whispered to herself. Then she said, "I think I have it! P–E–M–D–A–S! This is the order of operations," she said to the children, writing the following list on a piece of paper:

Parentheses
Exponents
Multiplication
Division
Addition
Subtraction

"I believe you're right," Al agreed. "We need to perform the operations inside the parentheses first, beginning inside the brackets."

"Well, one-half times 8 is inside of the brackets. I guess we should do this part first," the oldest child said. "One-half times 8 equals 4."

Al wrote the revised equation:

$$\text{Add } \frac{2 \times 3}{3} + (5 - 4)^2 - 2 \text{ teaspoons of salt}$$

"Now perform the operation that is inside the parentheses," Gebra prompted.

"Five minus 4 equals 1," the children said in unison as Al rewrote the recipe:

$$\text{Add } \frac{(2)\,(3)}{3} + (1)^2 - 2 \text{ teaspoons of salt}$$

"Next comes the exponent," prompted Gebra.

"One multiplied by itself is 1 times 1. And 1 times 1 is 1!" said a 13-year-old, sharing his knowledge.

$$\text{Add } \frac{(2)\,(3)}{3} + 1 - 2 \text{ teaspoons of salt}$$

"Now we multiply," several children said at once. "Two times 3 equals 6."

$$\text{Add } \frac{6}{3} + 1 - 2 \text{ teaspoons of salt}$$

"Now we divide. Six divided by 3 equals 2." The children were gaining confidence now.

Add 2 + 1 – 2 teaspoons of salt

"Next we add. Two plus 1 equals 3."

Add 3 – 2 teaspoons of salt

"And finally we subtract," almost everyone joined in.

"Three minus 2 equals 1. We need to add one teaspoon of salt, not 2,351!" The children giggled as they spoke.

"And we can know the order of operations by remembering 'Please excuse my dear Aunt Sally,'" one small child said.

"This way of remembering is called a *mnemonic*, or memory device," Al explained. "By the way, the first 'm' in the word *mnemonics* is silent."

"Let's make up our own mnemonics!" several children said at once. One by one they began shouting out their original memory devices for P–E–M–D–A–S:

> *"Pink Elephants Might Dance After Sunset."*
> *"Plan (for) Eighty Mean Dragons at Supper."*

Al and Gebra laughed as the children came up with other mnemonics. "I just noticed something," Al said. "The order of operations is the reverse of our travels. We just learned about parentheses this morning, but we solve for what's inside the parentheses first. Yesterday we learned about exponents. Before that it was multiplication and division, and before that, subtraction and addition."

"Good observation," replied Gebra. "It appears that the order of operations starts with the most complex procedures and moves toward the simpler ones."

"But I'm afraid *our* journey is going from the simple to the complex," said Al. "Let's see what's in store for us in the next kingdom."

Between the Kingdoms: Isolating X

Between the Kingdoms: Simplifying Expressions

The Eighth Kingdom
Solving for X

Moans of pain were all that Al and Gebra could hear from the fields surrounding the Eighth Kingdom.

"What's wrong?" Al asked the first person he encountered.

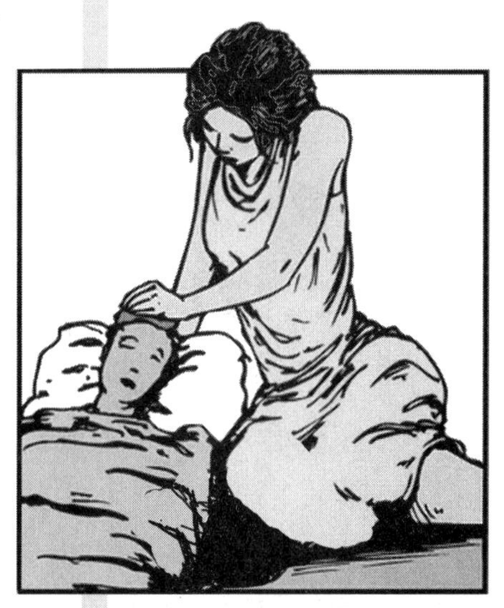

"We don't know for sure. Everyone is gradually becoming ill. We think there might be some poison in the drinking water," the person managed to say between moans. "Can you help us?"

"We'll need some of your water," Gebra answered. "We need to isolate the poison."

While waiting for the water sample to be delivered, Al and Gebra wrote a formula.

X = poison

X + pure water = poisonous water

"Whatever we do to one side of the equation, we must do to the other side as well," Al said, thinking aloud. "If we remove the pure water, we can isolate X."

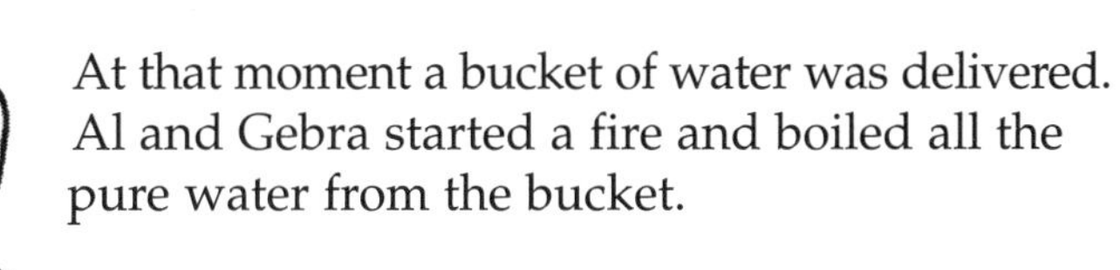

At that moment a bucket of water was delivered. Al and Gebra started a fire and boiled all the pure water from the bucket.

"Look at this substance in the bottom of the bucket," said Gebra. "It's lead. This is what is making everyone sick."

"We have been dumping our broken lead objects into the well," a woman nearby admitted.

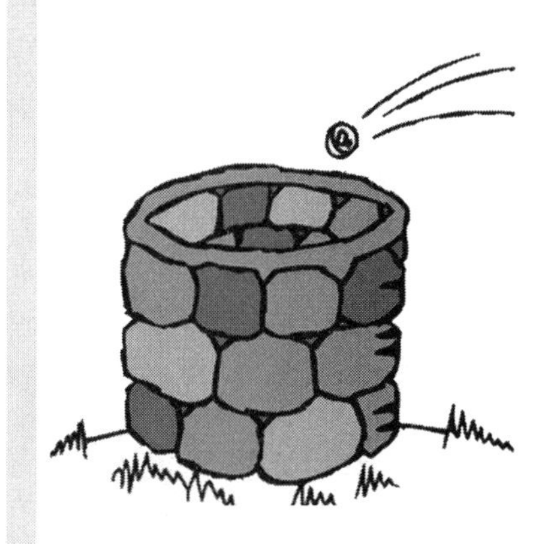

"We need to dig you a new well, and everyone must understand that no lead objects can be dropped into it," Al explained. "Then everyone should get better."

"Thank you," someone shouted from the crowd. "When we are healthy we can return to the castle. But it's no safer in there than it is out here in the fields."

"What's happening inside?" Al asked.

"Two fire-breathing dragons—an eastern dragon and a western dragon—have besieged the kingdom," said an elderly gentleman. "The only way to overcome the eastern dragon is for someone to pull the sword from the huge stone in the center of the courtyard. The brilliant shine from the sword will drive the dragon away."

"Then why doesn't someone do it?" Gebra asked.

"Because the person who removes the stone must say the secret code while grasping the hilt, and no one knows the entire code. One number is missing. We know the first three parts are 18, 27, and 32. But no one can remember the fourth number."

"We also know that the four numbers, when added together, equal 183," another woman continued.

"We can figure this out," said Al. "We'll let the variable X represent the missing number." He scribbled in the sand as he spoke.

$$18 + 27 + 32 + X = 183$$

"First we must combine like terms," Gebra added. "Eighteen plus 27 plus 32 equals 77." Al wrote as Gebra computed:

$$77 + X = 183$$

"If we subtract 77 from the left side we must also subtract it from the right side," she explained as she wrote:

$$X + 77 - 77 = 183 - 77$$

"By doing this we can isolate X," Al continued.

$$X = 106$$

"The final number of the secret code is 106," Al announced.

A thick cloud of smoke created a ceiling over their heads as Al and Gebra, followed by several of the people from the field, entered the courtyard. "That smoke is from the eastern dragon's breath," a man explained.

"It will serve as good cover for someone to make it to the sword," Gebra said. "I wish the smoke was a little thicker ... I know what I'll do." Gebra walked out into full view of the dragon and shook her fist at him.

"You coward!" she yelled. "Why don't you come down here and fight like a brave dragon?"

The words angered the dragon so that the fire and smoke grew thicker. Within seconds the smoke was so dense that no one could see more than a foot away. Under the cover of the smoke, Gebra felt her way to the stone in the center of the courtyard, climbed to the top of the rock, and grasped the handle of the sword. "Eighteen, 27, 32, 106," she called out loudly, and in an instant the sword was freed from the rock. The shine from the blade was dazzling. All the people in the courtyard fell to the ground, pressing their hands over their eyes.

Within seconds all was quiet, and the smoke began to clear. "Look," a child said, pointing toward the sky. "There is no dragon to the east."

"But the dragon to the west is still there," someone else warned. The western dragon was angrily looking for his eastern friend, his breath growing hotter and hotter.

"How do we get rid of him?" asked Al.

"This one is more complicated," a very old man said, stroking his beard. "This code is different. It is 18, 26, 104, and a fourth part that no one can remember. All these numbers must be added together. Then they must be divided by two. The total is 98."

Al quickly wrote:

$$\frac{18 + 26 + 104 + X}{2} = 98$$

"We need to combine like terms again," Gebra added. "18 + 26 + 104 equals 148. Now we have $\frac{148 + X}{2} = 98$."

"If we multiply both sides by two, we can cancel out the dividend," said Al, speaking as Gebra wrote:

$$2\left(\frac{148 + X}{2}\right) = 2(98)."$$

"Now we have 148 + X = 196," he continued. "We need to subtract 148 from both sides. So, 148 + X – 148 = 196 – 148," Al continued, talking as fast as he could.

"And that means X = 48," Gebra said, completing the equation. "The final number of the secret code is 48."

"Run to the tallest tower and throw a stone at the western dragon while yelling the code," a voice called out.

"I hope she's right," Al called over his shoulder as he took off running up the steps.

"Eighteen, 26, 104, 48," Al shouted while throwing the stone with all his might. The stone struck its mark—right between the western dragon's eyes. In a giant puff he was gone.

"Wait, we want to reward you for your good work," voices shouted from the crowd as Al and Gebra mounted their horses and started toward the drawbridge.

"We can't wait," they responded. "We're on our way to the Valley of Rest. We have six more castles to visit and only seven days left, and we need a day's rest before continuing our journey."

Al and Gebra disappeared almost as quickly as the western dragon had.

In the Valley of Rest, Al and Gebra
relaxed
and amused each other with riddles.

Between the Kingdoms: Riddle One

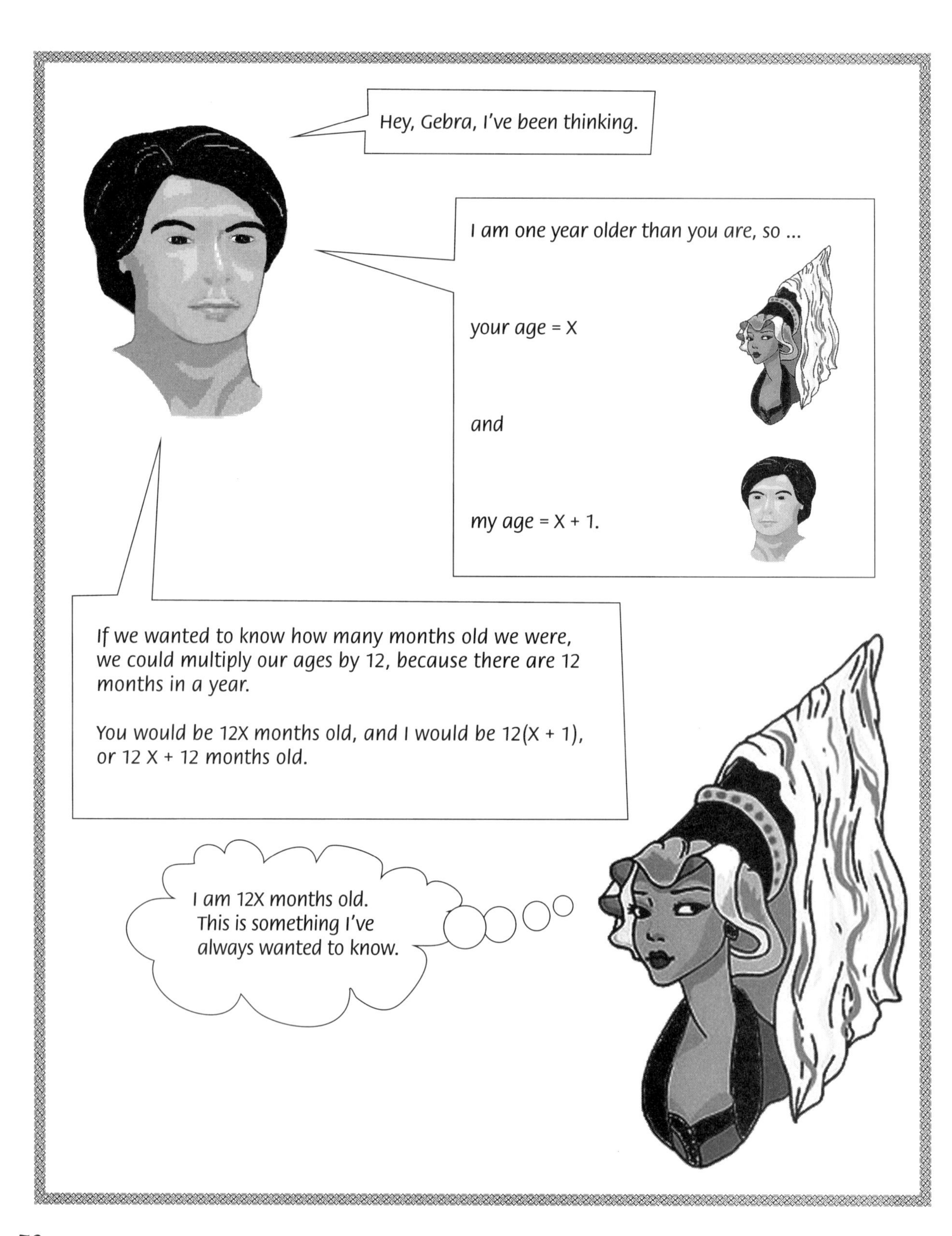

Between the Kingdoms: Riddle Two

Between the Kingdoms: Riddle Three

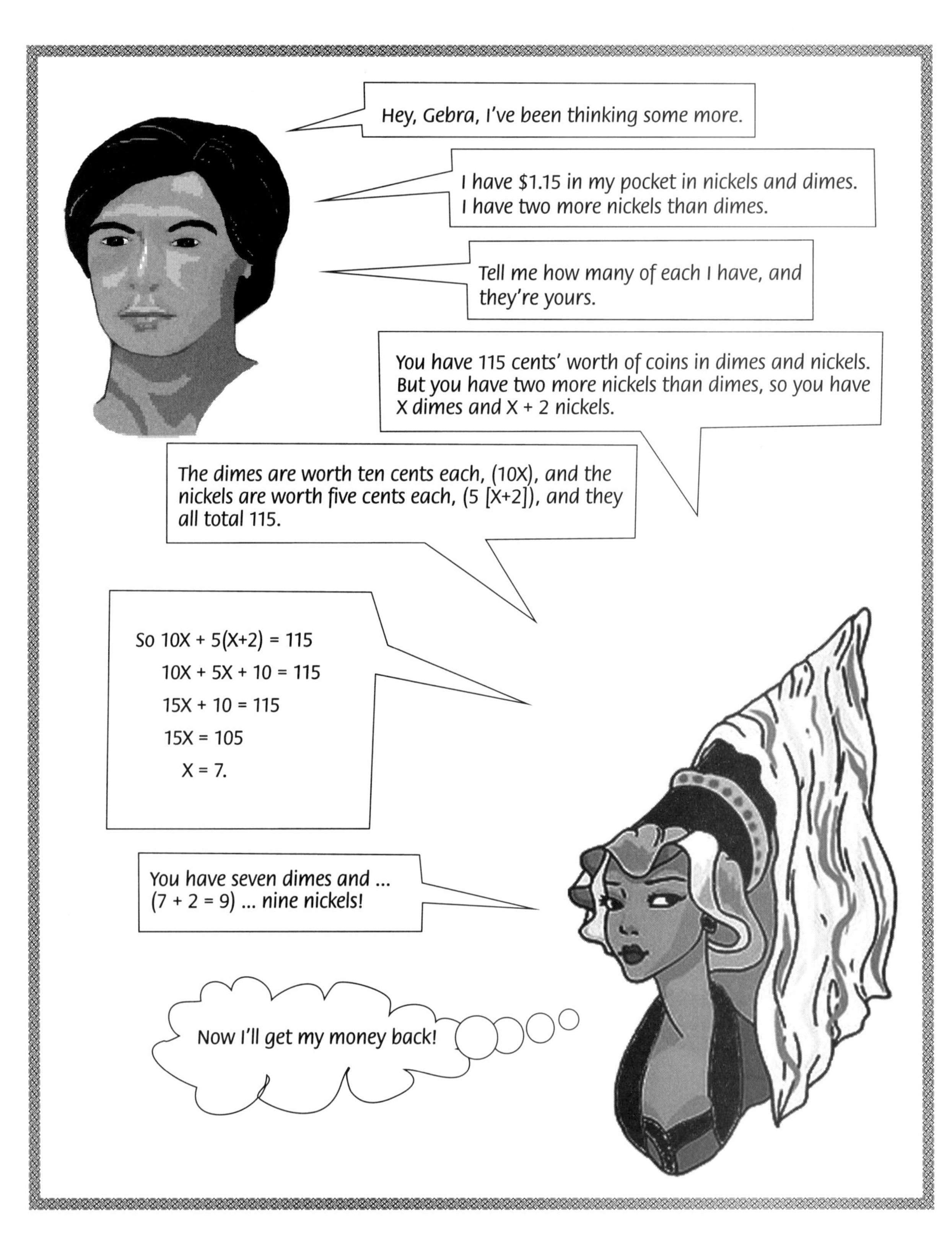

Between the Kingdoms: Riddle Four

The Ninth Kingdom
The Area of a Circle

Just outside the walls of the Ninth Kingdom, Al and Gebra were stunned to see a knight in shining armor riding around and around a tree.

"What in the world are you doing?" Gebra asked.

"My horse only goes in circles," the man replied.

"What is your name?"

"My name is Sir Cumference," the knight said proudly. "Do you want to know the distance around the base of that hill? I can measure it for you." Sir Cumference took off, riding a huge circle around a distant mountain.

"It's exactly 12 miles," said Sir Cumference when he returned and began riding around and around Al and Gebra.

"Is this what you do for a living—measure the distance around circles?" Al asked.

"It's what I do best, especially since my horse can't do anything else," Sir Cumference replied.

"Well, we'll name the distance around a circle after you, Sir Cumference. We'll name it the 'circumference,'" Gebra decided.

Circumference: the distance around a circle

"Can you get your horse to go up the drawbridge?" asked Al.

"Sure. I can ride around and around you all the way up," Sir Cumference assured them.

Just as the three of them were ready to ascend the drawbridge, they saw a woman walking straight toward the castle. "Hello," Al said.

"Hello. My name is Di. I measure the distance across the centers of circles," the woman answered. "Right now I'm measuring the distance across the middle of this round field."

"Are you a professional?" Gebra asked.

"No, I'm an amateur," the woman replied.

"So you're Di the Amateur. And you measure the distance across the centers of circles. Well, then, we'll name the distance across the center of a circle after you. We'll name it 'di-amateur,'" said Gebra, smiling.

Diameter: the distance across the center of a circle

"Diameter!" replied the woman. "I like it! The distance across the center of a circle is named after me—diameter."

"Would you like to go inside the castle with us?" requested Al. "We might need your help."

"Sure," answered Di.

"I'll go too!" Al and Gebra turned toward the voice to see a man lying in the grass nearby.

"Oh, no! Not you!" said Di, glaring. "Don't take him along. He's lazy. He's supposed to measure the distance across the middles of circles also, but he never does his job. He always stops halfway through."

"What is your name? asked Gebra.

"Ray," the man responded, halfway sitting up as he spoke. "My name is Ray. Ray Dius."

"And you measure half the distance across the middle of a circle …" Al clarified.

"My intentions are good," said Ray Dius with a half-smile.

"Well, Mr. Ray Dius, we'll name the distance from the edge to the center of a circle after you. We'll call it the 'Ray Dius,' or 'radius,'" Gebra said.

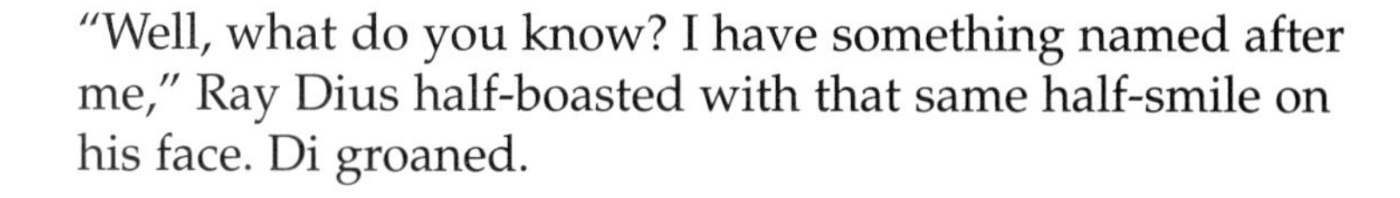

"Well, what do you know? I have something named after me," Ray Dius half-boasted with that same half-smile on his face. Di groaned.

"Let's go inside and see how the five of us can help the people in this kingdom," Al requested of everyone.

Sir Cumference yelled, "Charge!" and started riding circles around Al and Gebra as they climbed the drawbridge. Di the Amateur headed straight across the center of the courtyard. Ray Dius half-yawned and began taking half-steps behind the others.

Just inside the gate a lady shouted, "Pies! $3.14. Buy your pies from me. Just $3.14 each."

In the center of the courtyard, a group of people pointed to the ground where they stood arguing.

"What's the problem?" Sir Cumference asked while riding around and around one group of arguers.

"Problem?! You mean *problems!* We have three problems," a woman answered, waving three fingers in the air. "I'll tell you the first problem. We need to build a moat, but we don't know the distance around our fortress."

"Never fear! Sir Cumference is here!" shouted Sir Cumference as he rode around the fortress wall. "The distance around the outer circle of the fortress is exactly four miles, and the distance around a circle is named after me—circumference!" announced Sir Cumference proudly upon his return.

"Now for the next problem," a short woman raised her hand for attention. "We want to pave a road straight across the circular courtyard, but we don't know how long the road needs to be."

"My turn!" Di the Amateur joined the conversation as she ran toward the drawbridge. After carefully pacing the distance across the middle of the courtyard she announced, "The diameter of the courtyard circle is 200 feet."

"Our turn!" another group of arguers roared from nearby. "We want to pave the courtyard, but we need to know the area of the circle inside the castle walls so we'll know how much cement to order."

Al and Gebra looked at one another. "We don't have anyone with us to show us how to find the area of a circle," Gebra said. The entire courtyard fell silent.

Suddenly Ray's voice could be heard from near the pie stand. "Pie are square!" he was saying to the pie lady. In his hands he held two pies, each of which he had nibbled into a square shape. "Pie are square! Just $3.14 each," he added with a grin.

"No, pies are round," said the pie lady, giggling and tickling Ray's chin.

"Pie are square," he said, chuckling back at her. "Get your pies here."

"What a half-wit," said Di, rolling her eyes in disgust.

"No, he's right!" Al joined in. "I read about this once in an ancient document. There is a mathematical symbol that looks like this." Al drew the π symbol on the ground. "It's called pi. Pi is the name of a number, and that number is 3.14," he added, a triumphant smile on his face.

"Pie is a number?" someone asked.

"No, not pie—p-i." He spelled the letters separately. "Pi stands for 3.14," explained Al patiently. "The formula for

the area of a circle is πr^2, just as Ray Dius is saying. The variable r stands for radius, and π stands for 3.14."

"So, if Ray finds us the radius of the courtyard circle," Sir Cumference continued, "we will square the radius, then multiply the product by 3.14. The answer will be the area of the circle." Sir Cumference leaned back in his saddle and crossed his arms.

Once again the courtyard was silent except for more giggles and calls of "Pie are square! Just $3.14 each!" coming from the pie stand. After much encouragement Ray measured the radius of the courtyard, the pie lady by his side. "The radius is 100 feet," he announced.

"I could have told you that; the radius is half the diameter!" said Di the Amateur, looking disgusted. "The area of a circle $= \pi r^2$. So the area of this circle is:

$(3.14)(100 \text{ feet})^2 = (3.14)(10,000) = 31,400$ square feet."

"Hail, Sir Cumference and Lady Di the Amateur," the crowd cheered. At that moment the wisest person in the kingdom walked forward. "You will be rewarded for your wisdom with formulas of your own," she said. "The formulas for the distance around a circle shall include the circumference, the diameter, and the radius. The formulas shall be $C = 2\pi r$, and $C = \pi d$."

"Thank you," Sir Cumference and Di the Amateur said humbly. Ray Dius didn't hear the conversation. He was too busy eating pie and flirting with the pie lady.

"I think they can take it from here," whispered Gebra as she and Al paused at the drawbridge to look back before departing for the next kingdom.

The Tenth Kingdom

Distance = Rate Multiplied by Time

When they entered the Tenth Kingdom, Al and Gebra saw a very unusual sight. A handsome young knight was standing at the foot of a tall tower. At the top of the tower was a beautiful young princess. She had her head stuck out of a window with her long black hair hanging toward the ground. Her hair was so long it was just 18 inches above the reach of the young knight. Both the knight and the princess looked very ... bored.

"What's up?" Al asked the knight.

"Her hair," the knight responded. "It's up too high for me to reach."

Al and Gebra sat on their horses and looked at the knight, puzzled by what he had said. Finally Gebra looked up at the princess. "What is your name?" she asked.

"Daisy Rose Tigerlily, but you may call me D.R.T. for short," the princess replied.

"Nice to meet you, D.R.T.," said Al, tipping his hat toward the princess, "but I didn't quite understand what the knight was talking about." Al spoke again to the knight. "Did you say that her hair is too high for you to reach?"

"Yes," said the knight. "I'm supposed to rescue the princess from this tower. I was told I could climb up her hair to get to the top. But her hair is 18 inches too short for me to reach, so I'm waiting for it to grow longer."

"I see," Gebra said, clearing her throat. Looking up, she called out to the princess: "How fast does your hair grow?"

"Two inches each month," the princess answered.

"I'm afraid you might be here for a while," Gebra warned the knight.

"How do you know?" the knight asked.

"Well, let's use the princess's name as a way to look at this," Al explained. "Her name is Daisy Rose Tigerlily, or D.R.T. for short. Let's pretend the D stands for Distance, the R stands for Rate, and the T stands for Time."

D = Distance
R = Rate
T = Time

"I don't get it," the knight said.

"You want to know the distance her hair will grow in a certain length of time," continued Gebra. "This will tell you the rate at which her hair will grow."

"Now I get it," the knight finished the formula. "The distance her hair will grow is equal to the rate multiplied by the time it has to grow."

$$D = RT$$

"Six months is all the time I have," said the knight as he began scribbling on the ground. "Let's see how much her hair will grow in six months."

D = RT
D = 2 inches each month times 6 months
D = 12 inches

"What?! Her hair will grow only 12 inches in six months? But it's 18 inches too short. Sorry," the knight shouted up to the princess, "I don't have enough time to rescue you." The knight waved farewell to the princess, mounted his horse, and rode away.

"I wonder if he ever considered sitting on his horse so he could reach her hair more easily," Al whispered to Gebra.

"Never mind. I'll rescue myself," the princess said. She pulled her long locks up into the tower and tied the ends of her hair to a rock. She then climbed down the rope that her hair created. When she got to the end of her hair, she was dangling several feet above the ground. She reached into her pocket, retrieved a knife, cut her hair just above her head, and dropped to the ground.

"Not bad, D.R.T.," Al said, smiling.

Suddenly a streak of lightning lighted the sky. Five seconds later a clap of thunder shook the air around them. "The sound of thunder travels about 1,000 feet a second," observed the princess. "We saw the lightning, then five seconds later we heard the thunder: D = RT; D = (1,000)(5). The streak of lightning was about 5,000 feet away from us."

"The next kingdom is 150 miles away," said Gebra, looking out across the fields. She began sketching in the sand. "Our horses can travel at 25 miles an hour," she added.

$D = RT$
$D = 150$ miles
$R = 25$ miles an hour
$150 = 25T$

$$\frac{150}{25} = \frac{25T}{25}$$

$6 = T$

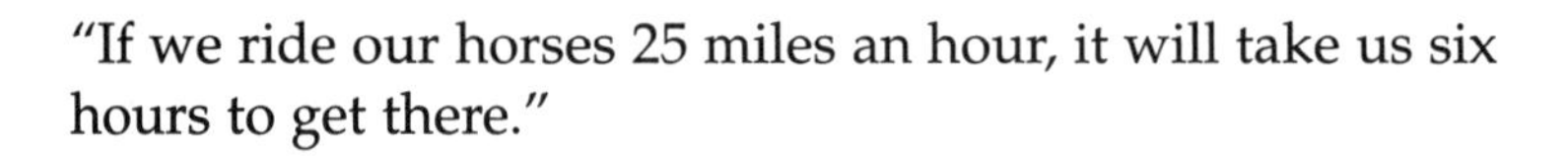

"If we ride our horses 25 miles an hour, it will take us six hours to get there."

"Listen," a voice whispered in a sudden breeze.

"That voice … it sounds familiar," Gebra said, suddenly turning pale.

"And where is that breeze coming from?" Al asked, looking in all directions.

"Look up, in the branches of the trees." The princess pointed upward as she spoke.

"It's that man again," Gebra whispered, her voice trembling.

"Listen," the voice repeated.

As they sat motionless under the canopy of leaves, Al, Gebra, and the princess heard a rustling sound.

"That was the sound of a pigeon being freed from its cage, and it is flying toward you," the voice said. "The pigeon has a message for you. You must get the message before daybreak or you will die."

"How fast can the pigeon fly?" Al asked.

"The pigeon can fly 50 miles an hour," responded the voice.

"But it's only two hours before daybreak!" Gebra screamed. "If the pigeon flies 50 miles an hour, it can fly only 100 miles in two hours, and we're 150 miles away."

"If you meet the pigeon part of the way, maybe you can make it," the princess said encouragingly.

"Our horses can run 25 miles an hour, and the pigeon can fly 50 miles an hour," Al thought aloud. "Can the distance of the pigeon plus the distance of the horses make the trip in two hours?" Al wrote in the sand:

D_1 = the distance the pigeon can fly. D_2 = the distance the horses can run.

$D_1 + D_2 = 25 + 50 = 75$

"Together the pigeon and the horses can travel 75 miles each hour," he said. "That's the rate all of us will travel each hour: R = 75."

"We also know the distance we need to travel," added Gebra. "We need to travel 150 miles. Now we need to know how much time it will take us."

$D = RT$

$150 = 75t$

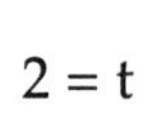

$\frac{150}{75} = 75t$

$2 = t$

"It will take us two hours to travel 150 miles," Gebra said as she put her foot into the stirrup of her saddle. "And that's exactly how much time we have."

"Farewell, and good luck!" the princess shouted as Al and Gebra rode away.

Two hours later Al and Gebra were 50 miles closer to the next kingdom. "Look! There it is!" Gebra pointed toward a tiny dot silhouetted against the moon. Although Al stretched his arm out to provide a landing place for the pigeon, it settled instead on Gebra's saddle. Al gingerly took a small note from its claws.

"Look in your saddlebag," the note began. "You will find what looks like a small rock. It isn't. It will explode when touched by the rays of the morning sun."

Al quickly reached into Gebra's saddlebag and found the object, which did indeed look like a rock. "I can't throw it far enough," Al said desperately as the sun's rays began to peek over the mountaintop.

Gebra jumped down from her horse and picked up a long, heavy stick. "Pitch it into the air," she said.

Al pitched the artificial rock just over their heads. Like a batter in baseball, Gebra swung the branch with all her might, striking the object as it descended. She sent it flying over the treetops.

"Hit the deck," yelled Al.

Face down on the ground with their arms over their heads, Al and Gebra heard a loud explosion, and almost immediately dirt and twigs settled around them.

"That was close," Gebra whispered.

They stood up, dusted the debris from their hair and clothes, and were once again on their way.

"Meeting Daisy Rose Tigerlily and knowing that D = RT saved our lives," said Al. "Let's go."

The Eleventh Kingdom

Reciprocals

A banner reading "The Kingdom of Riddles" rippled in the breeze above the walls of the Eleventh Kingdom.

"This should be fun," said Al excitedly.

Eagerly anticipating what might lie ahead, Al and Gebra guided their horses straight to the center of the courtyard. Suddenly a loud clanking noise filled the air. In less than a second a round wall of steel bars surrounded them. Al and Gebra ran from one bar to another, shaking the cold metal cage, trying to find an escape.

Suddenly people came from everywhere, silently moving closer and closer. Each person carried a lighted torch.

"I thought this was the Kingdom of Riddles," Gebra shouted, clearly upset by the unyielding steel bars.

"It is." A whisper echoed through the silence as the torches grew still. At that moment a voice bellowed from the balcony. "So, you like riddles. I have a riddle for you! Listen to this:

> **"You'll die right here in the middle,**
> **Unless you solve your riddle.**
>
> **"But one riddle will not do—**
> **We have five for you!"**

"This sounds serious," Al whispered to Gebra. "OK, we're ready to play," he said to the crowd.

"The first riddle is for you," said a man standing nearby. He looked at Al as he spoke:

> **"We'll tell you our name in verse.**
> **Our product is always the first."**

"'We'll tell you our name in verse. Our product is always the first.'" Al repeated the words. "When we multiply two numbers together, the answer is called the product. This riddle must have something to do with multiplication."

"'Our product is always the first,'" Gebra thought aloud. "The first what? The first letter of the alphabet is A, but when we multiply we use numbers, not letters. The first number is 1."

"You're right. Maybe when the riddle says our product is always the first, it's talking about multiplying two numbers together that have a product of 1," Al said.

"That makes sense," said Gebra, then asked: "What factors have a product of 1?"

"Well, 1 times 1 equals 1," said Al.

Before Al and Gebra could finish their conversation, a pair of women whispered, "We'll give you a hint: Your answer cannot wait. One of us is Eight."

"If one of you is named Eight, what is the other one's name?" Gebra asked. "What number multiplied by 8 equals 1?"

"I know!" she said after thinking for a few seconds. "One-eighth! One-eighth times 8 equals 1: 1/8 X 8 = 1. Your name is Eight, and the other person in your pair is named One-Eighth."

Two more women whispered, "One of us is Two. Do you know what to do?"

"One-half times 2 equals 1: 1/2 X 2 = 1," Al whispered back to them. "If your name is Two, the other person's name is One-Half."

"East, south, west, or north, one of us is One-Fourth," another pair whispered.

"One-fourth times 4 equals 1: 1/4 X 4 = 1. If your name is One-Fourth, the other person's name is Four," Gebra answered.

"Enough! So you have figured out the names of individuals. Now you must tell us what we call factors that equal 1," a voice shouted from the balcony.

"What do we call two numbers that equal 1 when multiplied together?" Al shook the bars as he thought out loud. "Let's think about the original riddle again. 'We'll tell you our name in verse. Our product is always the first.'"

Offered Gebra: "Maybe the name for two factors that equal 1 is in the first line of the riddle: 'We'll tell you our name in verse.'"

"The riddle says it will tell us the name. Then it says 'in verse,'" Al added.

"'In verse.' Maybe this is the answer. 'In verse.' Maybe they aren't two words at all. Perhaps they are one word—'inverse,'" said Gebra.

"Two numbers that, when multiplied together, equal 1 are called 'multiplicative inverse,'" Al shouted toward the balcony.

"I'm impressed!" the same voice bellowed back from the balcony. "But before you have completely answered our first riddle, you must tell us another word for inverse."

Al shook his fist toward the balcony and yelled, "We answered your riddle. This isn't fair! I will get back at you! I will reciprocate."

"You're right! Another word for inverse is 'reciprocal,'" the voice boomed. "Close enough. You are ready for your second riddle."

"The next riddle is yours," a very tall man said to Gebra.

> **"These numbers are not our heroes.**
> **They always add up to zeros."**

"This riddle is about adding," said Gebra, again thinking aloud. "It's about numbers that add up to zero, like (+6) + (-6). The sum is zero. But what do we call them?"

"I don't know. Inverse worked last time; let's try it again," suggested Al. "Only this time we'll call them additive instead of multiplicative."

"Two numbers that have a sum of zero are additive inverses of each other!" Gebra shouted toward the balcony.

"Right again," the man's voice boomed. "Now answer this one:

> **"Add a square and be square.**
> **Find the right angle and see square."**

"'Add a square and be square.' How do I add a square? And how would adding a square make me be square?" Gebra was almost in tears as she spoke.

"Let's stay calm," Al whispered. "The riddle says, 'Add a square and be square.' Maybe the word 'square' is referring to the power of 2—that type of square."

"So maybe the riddle means, 'Add a^2 and b^2.' And maybe the words 'see square' in the next line mean c^2," said Gebra, her face brightening.

"Add $a^2 + b^2$. Find the right angle and c^2," Al wrote on the palm of his hand. "A right triangle has a right angle."

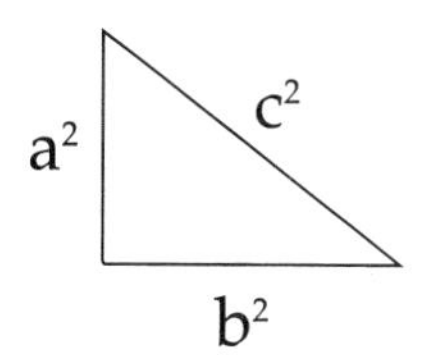

"That's it!" Gebra exclaimed as she sketched in the sand.

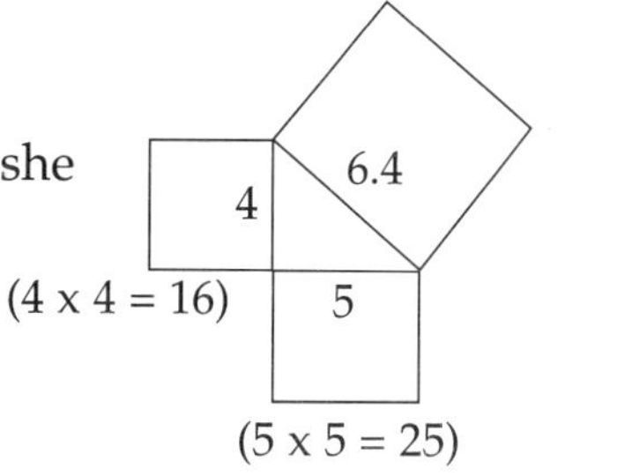

16 + 25 = 41

"If we add the lengths of the lines a^2 and b^2, we get the length of c^2, the hypotenuse. A^2 plus B^2 equals C^2!" Gebra shouted toward the balcony.

"So far, so good!" the voice responded. "But what do we call this theorem, $a^2 + b^2 = c^2$? Who discovered it?"

"This is pathetic!" Gebra yelled out in anger.

"That's right! It's the Pythagorean theorem," the voice said. "Once again, you're close enough. On to your fourth riddle."

"It's your turn again," the third man said to Al. Then he read:

"If you're in your prime,
There's no factoring any time."

"'If I'm in my prime,'" Al repeated, almost absently. "I'm 17 years old."

"'There's no factoring any time,'" Gebra continued. "Factors are numbers that are multiplied together. So if there's no factoring, then we need a number that has no factors, such as 17. There are no numbers, other than 17 and 1, that can be multiplied together to equal 17."

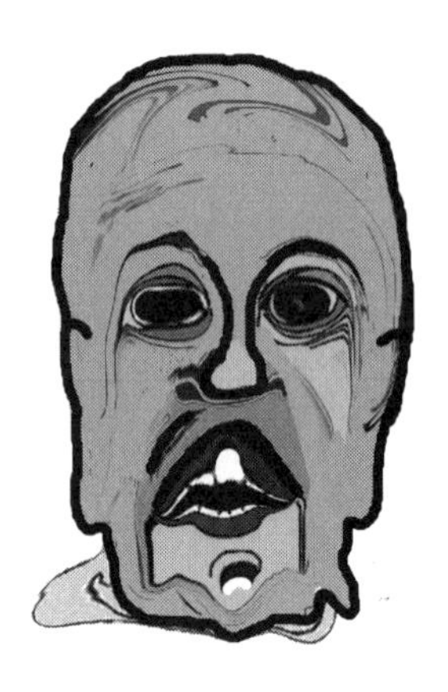

"So 17 isn't just a prime age; it's also a prime number. Numbers such as 3, 5, 7, 11, 13, and 17 don't have any factors that can be multiplied together to equal them. Numbers that cannot be factored are prime numbers." Al's voice was getting louder and louder as he thought it through. By the end, he was shouting toward the balcony.

"Four out of four!" came the voice. "We're all impressed. The next one's for you, young lady!" A new face appeared at the cage. Gebra stiffened. The man's voice was husky and low.

"While prime numbers slumber,
What is a composite number?"

"'While prime numbers slumber …'" Gebra again thought aloud. "Composite numbers must be numbers that are not prime."

"Numbers such as 6 aren't prime," added Al. "Two and 3 can be multiplied together to equal 6, so 6 is not a prime number."

"Composite numbers are numbers that aren't prime," Gebra shouted to the balcony.

The silence of grudging admiration greeted their final answer, and the steel cage lifted. Al and Gebra led their horses slowly toward the castle gate.

Between the Kingdoms: Axiom of Equality

The Twelfth Kingdom
Graphs

The Twelfth Kingdom was dark and silent as Al's and Gebra's horses climbed the drawbridge and stepped inside, a cool breeze greeting them as they paused just inside the castle walls. Silently they urged their horses forward, wondering if the entire kingdom had been deserted.

"Something's wrong," Gebra said quietly as they neared the center of the courtyard. In an instant, thousands of torches were lighted simultaneously, revealing bleachers packed with onlookers cheering loudly. Al's and Gebra's horses snorted and pranced in the center of the courtyard looking for an escape, but none could be found. The drawbridge was tightly closed.

"Welcome," a voice resounded across the courtyard. "The contest will begin at dawn. Be ready."

"What contest?" Al yelled, but his question was met with silence, and the courtyard went instantly dark. Only one small torch remained lit, and it was getting closer and closer. Finally the light was close enough for Al and Gebra to see the shining brown eyes of the torchbearer.

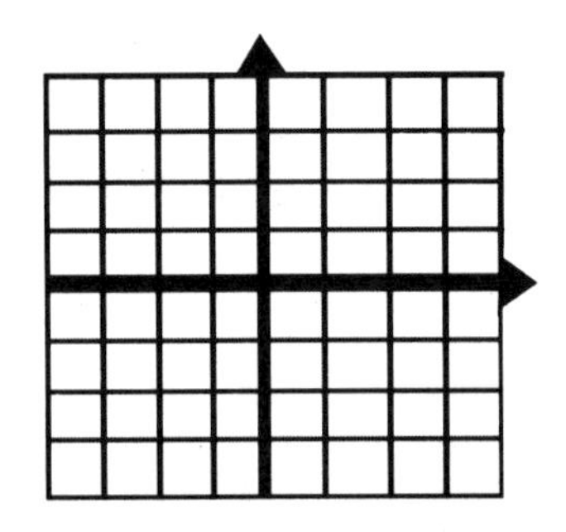

"Follow me," a deep voice demanded. Al and Gebra dismounted and, without speaking, followed the flame to a small, cold chamber. Once inside, the man slid his torch into a bracket on the wall, and it filled the room with shadows and highlights. The man turned toward Al. "Tomorrow you will stand before 64 doors, arranged like this," he said, holding up a diagram. "Where the lines cross is where the key will unlock the door.

"Behind one door will be a treasure of gold and jewels. If you choose this door, the treasure is yours. Behind the other 63 doors will be fire-breathing dragons. If you choose any one of those doors, you will be burned to death."

Without another word, the man turned and left the room. Al rushed to the door and tried to open it, but it was locked from the outside.

"Don't worry. We'll think of something," said Gebra, trying to comfort him. "Wait a minute ... I know! Tomorrow I will sit in the bleachers behind the doors, and I will signal you to let you know which door to choose."

"Good thinking," said Al. "But what signal will you use?"

"Let's think," said Gebra as she paced the cell. "Look, the mysterious man left the torch and the diagram." Gebra pulled the torch from the wall and held it near the grid.

"Look at these two bold lines," she whispered. "One cuts the grid in half horizontally, and the other cuts it in half vertically. We can call this point where the two bold lines cross the 'point of origin,' and we will call each quarter a 'quadrant.'"

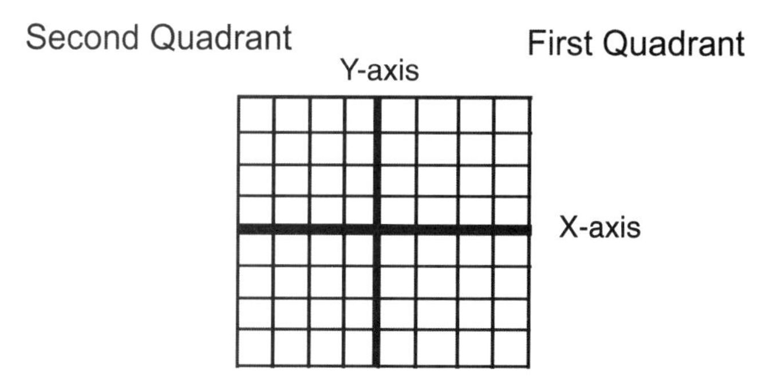

"Let's call this line the 'Y-axis,'" said Gebra, pointing to the bold vertical line. "So if the treasure is to the right of the Y-axis, I'll hold up a number like +1, +2, +3, or +4, and if it is to the left of the Y-axis, the number will be -1, -2, -3, or -4." The confidence in Gebra's voice gave Al some hope.

"And we'll call this the 'X-axis,'" said Al, warming to the task and pointing to the bold horizontal line. "You can write a second number on the sign. If the treasure is one row above the X-axis, the second number will be +1. If it's two rows above the X-axis, it will be +2. And if the treasure is below the X-axis, you'll hold up a sign that says -1, -2, -3, or -4, depending on the row the treasure is in.

"I'm starting to feel better," continued Al. "Let's practice to see if we can keep the pairs of numbers in order."

"OK, here's the first ordered pair," said Gebra, attempting to smile as she spoke. She held up a sign that read "(+2, -3)."

Starting at the point of origin, Al counted two lines to the right, then three lines down. "The point (+2, -3) would be right here," Al said, pointing to the diagram.

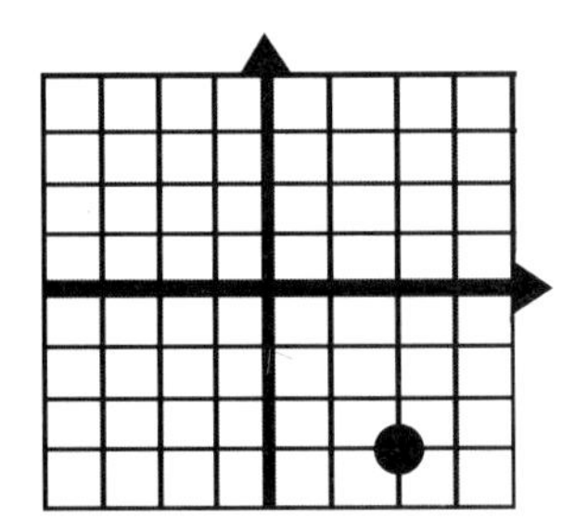

"How about this one?" Gebra said, holding up a sign that read "(-3, +4)."

Al returned to the point of origin, then counted three lines to the left and four lines up. "Here it is," he said, pointing to the grid. "I think we have our ordered pairs down pat."

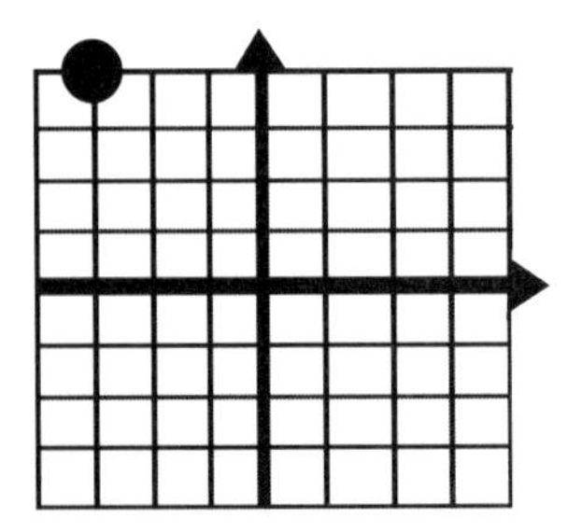

Al and Gebra sat in silence for the rest of the night, sleeping only fitfully, until the chamber door flew open and the mysterious man reappeared. Al distracted him with questions while Gebra disappeared into the crowded bleachers. The man led Al to the center of the courtyard and made him stand in front of a huge grid that looked exactly like the diagram from the night before.

"Choose your door!" a voice thundered. Al frantically looked for Gebra, but in the sea of screaming faces he could not find her. "You have 30 seconds," the voice warned.

"I choose … " Al tried to stall for time.

"Fifteen seconds!" Fourteen, 13, 12 … Al could feel the seconds ticking away. Finally, with five seconds to go, he saw Gebra wildly waving a sign in the air. The sign read "(+3, -2)."

"The first number stands for the X-axis, and it is positive, so I will move to the right three places," Al thought. He started at the point of origin and counted three rows to the right. The second coordinate was negative, so from there he counted two rows down.

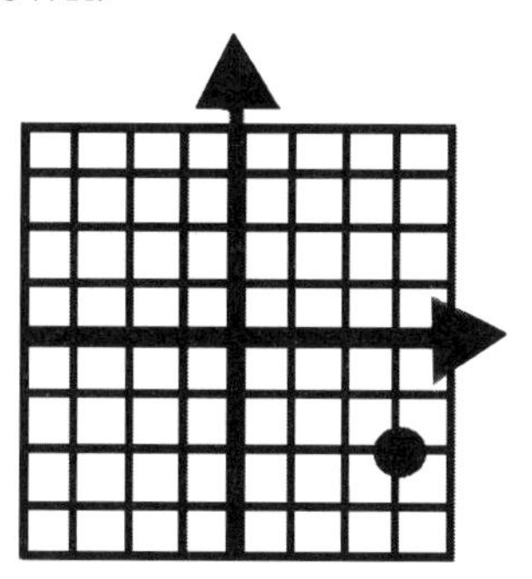

Al called the number of the door with just one second to go before time was up. The door flew open and sparkles from the glistening treasure danced around the room. The crowd cheered even louder than before.

The mysterious man helped Al tie the treasure bag to his saddle. "You are the first person ever to win this contest," he said. "The others before you had a burning desire to win, but then a dragon was soon hot on their heels. I'm glad you won. Both of you," he added. Then he smiled at Gebra. "By the way, where were you while he was deciding which door to choose?"

Gebra's face turned crimson, the color of fire.

"Ordered pairs are handy," the man continued. "I call a set of ordered pairs a relation."

Gebra blushed again, trying to think of something to say. "The first coordinate in an ordered pair is the domain, and the second one is the range," she blurted out, then added quietly: "Just in case you ever need to know."

"The domain and the range. You're pretty smart," the mysterious man smiled. "If a relation is such that no two ordered pairs within it have the same first coordinate, what do we call the relation?"

"What do you mean?" Gebra asked for clarification.

"An example would be (-2, -1) (1, 2) (-1, 0). None of the first coordinates—the domains, as you called them—are the same. What do we call this type of relation?"

"A function," said Gebra, smiling.

"Not bad," the man said.

As Gebra spurred her horse into action, she commented, "By the way, you look much better in the daylight. You should get out more often."

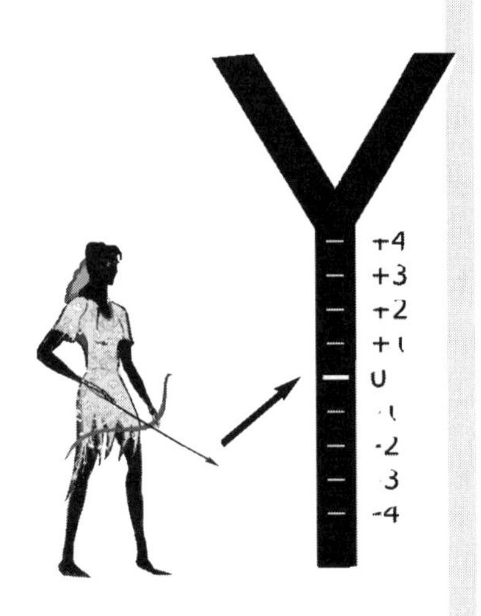

As they were leaving the Twelfth Kingdom, Al and Gebra heard a commotion in a nearby forest. "Let's see what's happening," suggested Gebra, pulling her horse's right rein. A short distance away they could see a small group of people preparing to practice their archery skills.

"Let's shoot toward that tree," said one of them, pointing to a tall Y-shaped oak. "We'll call the point where the arrow hits the tree the 'Y-intercept.'"

A tall, thin woman drew lines on the tree with values next to each line. "This is how we can keep track of where the tree and the arrow intersect," she said as she took 20 paces, gently stretched her bow, and let go. The arrow landed on the (+2) line.

"Your arrow intercepted the tree at +2," a helper reported, looking closely at the arrow.

The second archer released his arrow. It intercepted the Y at the -4 line.

The next archer pulled the string of her bow. "I'll intercept the Y with my arrow at the -1 mark," she predicted. Her arrow was right on target.

"I'm next!" Everyone recognized the voice of the court jester and laughed just to see him coming. Standing on his hands, the jester pulled his bowstring with his feet and sent his arrow toward the Y-tree. It intersected the Y at -3.

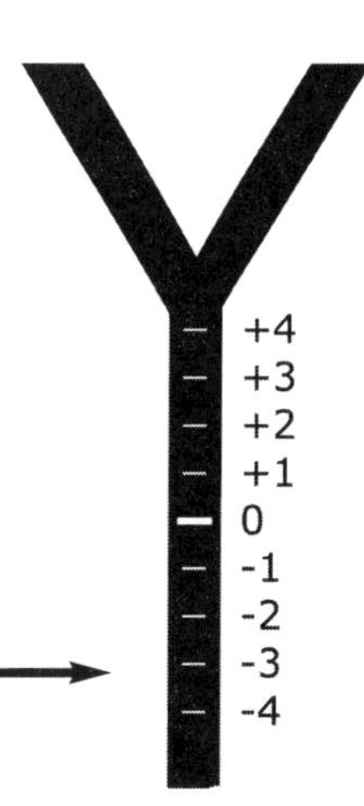

"Great shot!" cheered the crowd.

"After what we went through in the Twelfth Kingdom, we needed a little bit of fun," said Al as he and Gebra urged their horses away from the forest.

The Thirteenth Kingdom
Slope

"Listen! There's quite a commotion inside the Thirteenth Kingdom," Gebra said as she spurred her horse onto the drawbridge. "It looks like a dragon show!" she shouted with excitement when she was close enough to see the action.

"We need help judging this dragon contest," the head judge said to Al and Gebra as they rode by. "Do you know how to judge dragons?"

"What kinds of dragons are entered in your contest?" Al asked.

"Risers and runners," the judge responded, "but we don't have anything on which they can run or rise. What must we do?"

"Remember the grid," Gebra whispered to Al. Turning to the judge, she said, "I think we can help. We'll be ready by tomorrow morning."

The next morning Al and Gebra presented the panel of judges with a grid that looked very similar to the one they saw in the Twelfth Kingdom.

The head judge looked at Al and Gebra's work, then made an announcement to the crowd of spectators. "I have instructed my assistants to explain the rules of the contest, so please listen carefully," he said. The judge then handed a megaphone to Gebra.

"The dragons must perform in pairs," Gebra began. "One runner and one riser will comprise each pair of dragons. The runner will run, and the riser will rise in a pattern across this grid."

"These are the rules of the contest," continued Al.

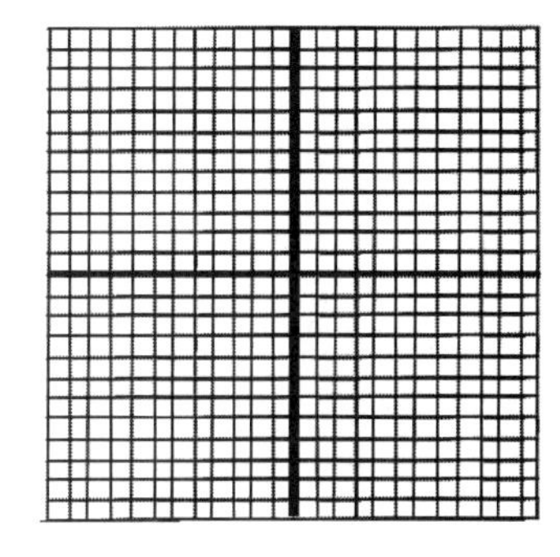

> *1) Each dragon trainer will draw one number from a bowl labeled X—and another from a bowl labeled Y.*
> *2) The dragons will start at the point of origin, which is where the X- and Y-axes intersect.*
> *3) The trainer will signal for the runner dragon to run on the grid. The runner shall cover a number of grid points equivalent to the number drawn from the X-bowl.*
> *4) The trainer will then signal for the riser dragon to rise on the grid a number of points equivalent to the number drawn from the Y-bowl.*
> *5) This will constitute one lap. The course must be repeated twice more, for a total of three laps, with each lap starting from the last set of coordinates. Each ordered pair of dragons will be evaluated according to how accurately the pair completes each lap.*

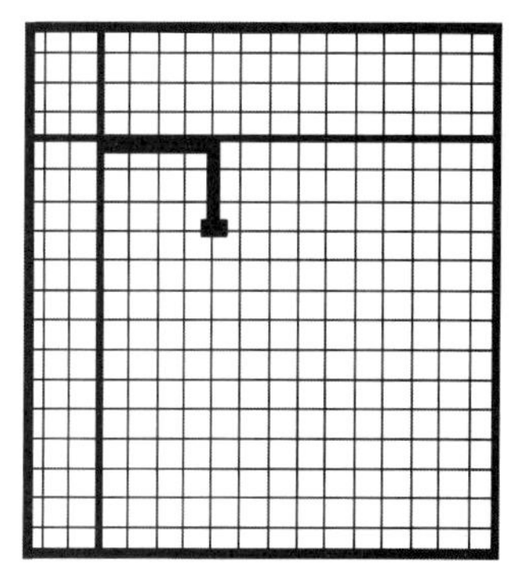

The first trainer reached into the X-bowl and drew the number +4. She signaled for her runner dragon to run four lines to the right.

Then she reached into the Y-bowl and drew -3. She signaled for the riser dragon to rise negative three lines on the grid.

The first lap was completed.

"The first heat is a success!" Al announced. "Now the riser and the runner must repeat this pattern two more times."

The crowd grew silent as the trainer signaled for the dragons to run and rise again. The runner dragon ran four more lines in a positive direction. The riser met her there and rose three lines in a negative direction. The orders were repeated until the grid looked like this:

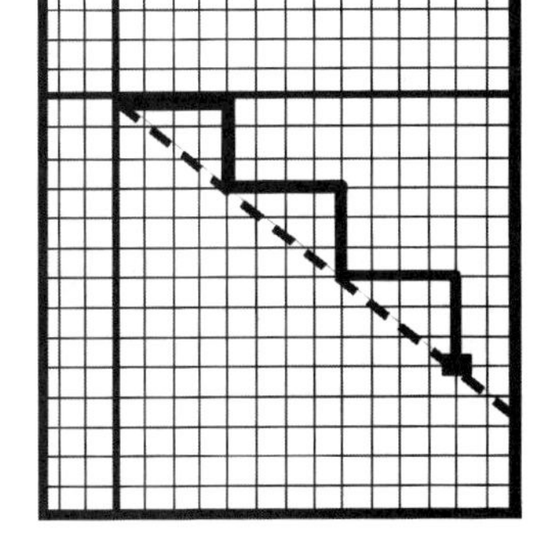

"A perfect performance," said Gebra, congratulating the first ordered pair. "The slope of the line that you ran is perfectly straight. The run is (+4) and the rise is (-3) every time. A perfect (+4, -3) slope."

The dragon trainer and her dragons took a bow.

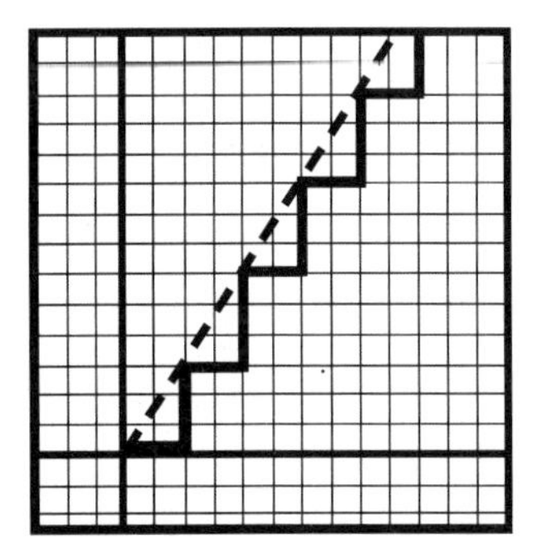

The second dragon trainer drew (+2) from the X-bowl and (+3) from the Y-bowl. He signaled for his runner dragon to run two spaces in a positive direction (+2). Then he signaled for his riser dragon to rise three lines in a positive direction (+3). After the third lap was completed, the dragons ran two more laps for good measure.

"A perfect run for another ordered pair. (+2, +3) slope of their line is flawless," announced Al through the megaphone.

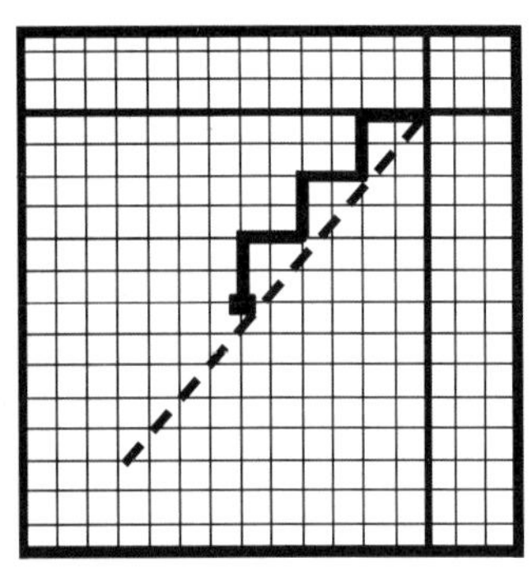

The third trainer's ordered pair of numbers was (-2, -2). "The runner must run two lines in a negative direction, then the riser must rise two lines in a negative direction," declared Gebra.

The third dragons' runs were perfect, showing a straight (-2, -2) slope.

The final trainer drew (-3) from the X-bowl and (-3) from the Y-bowl, for an ordered pair of (-3, -3).

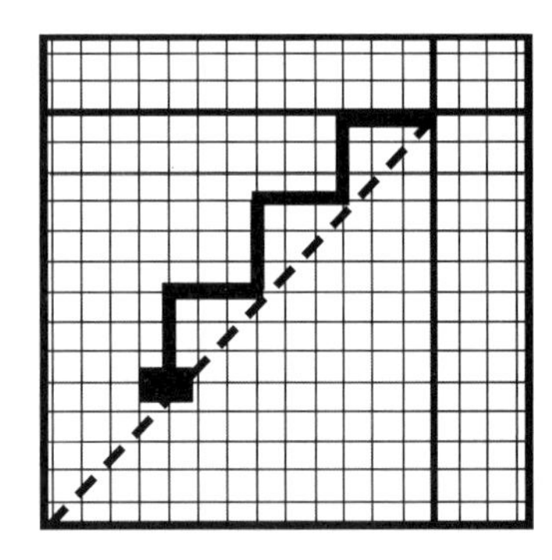

"Another perfect slope," the judge said when the dragons had completed all three laps. The judge and the crowd were ecstatic. The fourth grid looked like the one at right.

"I wish all problems could be this much fun to solve, but we still have one more kingdom to go," Al told the judge as he and Gebra mounted their horses, the cheers of the crowd ringing in their ears.

Between the Kingdoms: More Slope

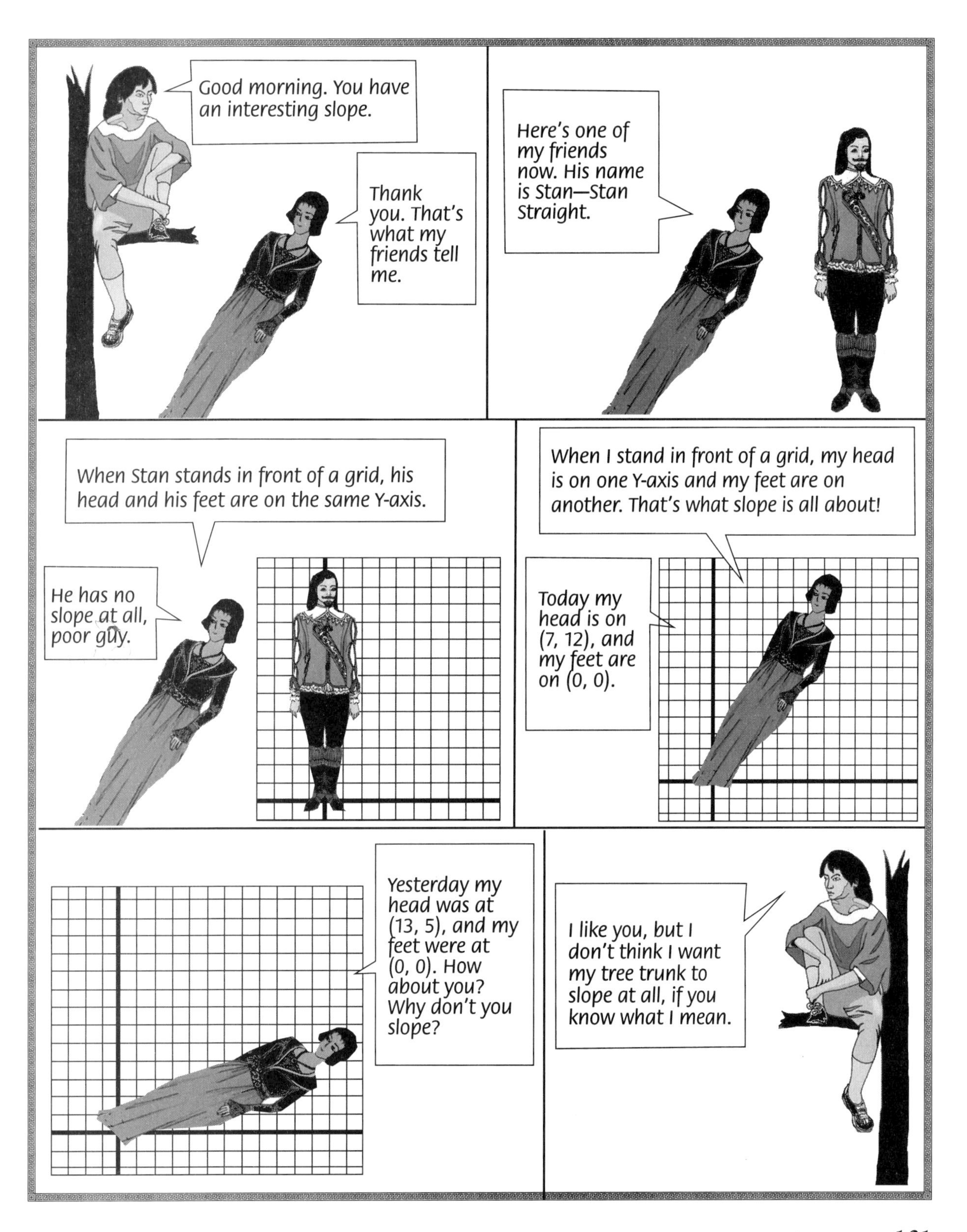

Between the Kingdoms: Measuring Slope

The Fourteenth Kingdom
Linear Equations

Al and Gebra's journey to the Fourteenth Kingdom took them through the middle of an ancient hardwood forest. "Look, Gebra," Al said, studying the trunk of a huge oak tree. "Some lovers have carved their initials into the bark of this tree. 'Y = MX + B.' What strange initials!"

No sooner had Al spoken these words than a tiny, very serious-looking man appeared from the far side of the tree. "They are not initials," the man rasped. "Y = MX + B is the formula for a straight line."

"Why would anyone ever need a formula for a straight line?" asked Al, amazement on his face.

The tiny man acted like he hadn't heard Al's question. "The M variable stands for the slope of the line," he said, pointing to the M in the formula.

"But, sir, why would the variable M stand for slope?" Gebra asked, trying to understand what the man was saying.

"Maybe a slope looks like it's **melting.** Maybe it looks like it's **moving.** I don't know!" The tiny man seemed exasperated, shrugging his bony shoulders and frowning as he spoke. "More than likely the word came from another language, when someone far away developed the formula for slope," he continued. "Anyway, the B variable stands for the point at which the line crosses the Y-axis," he continued.

"That point is called the Y-intercept," Gebra interjected, remembering an earlier kingdom.

Ignoring Gebra's comment, the tiny man said, "I've said enough. I have to go now." With these words he disappeared as mysteriously as he had come.

"That was strange," said Al with a laugh. "But remembering that $Y = MX + B$ is the formula for a straight line might not be a bad idea."

Al led his horse to the bank of a stream. As he bent down and cupped his hands to drink, a bright, glinting reflection caught his eye. He looked closer, then carefully removed a shiny object from the shallow water.

"It looks like a small treasure chest," he said, gingerly opening the hinged lid. Inside the box was a yellowed and crumpled piece of paper. "It's a map," said Al after a quick glance. "We don't have time to study it now; we need to move on to the Fourteenth Kingdom. We can take a closer look when we get there." Al tucked the paper into his vest pocket, mounted his steed, and motioned for Gebra to lead the way.

Inside the Fourteenth Kingdom, Al and Gebra could find no one except a young prince and his assistant. The pair stood gazing over the stone wall of the fortress.

"We're looking for buried treasure," the prince explained to Al and Gebra, the prince and his assistant continuing to survey the village below them. The village was neatly arranged, with one major thoroughfare running east and west and another running north and south. The prince said the east-west road was named X Street and the north-south road was named Y Street. Stone cottages dotted the alleyways in straight rows. In the yard of each cottage were women, men, and children digging in the dirt with handmade tools.

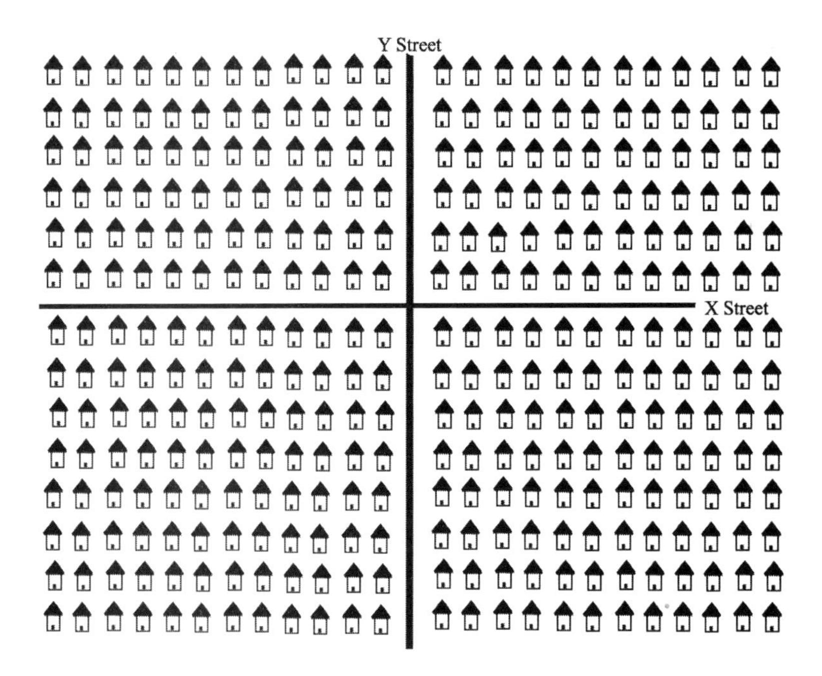

"According to legend," the prince continued, "a treasure was buried in the streets of this village hundreds of years ago. So far only one coin has been found because we can't locate the map showing where the remainder of the treasure was buried."

"Wait a minute!" Al gasped, pulling the yellowed paper from his vest pocket. "This might be it! I found this map by the creek less than an hour ago."

"This is wonderful!" said the suddenly excited prince. "Let me summon the villagers." He motioned for his assistant to signal a gathering. Within minutes, hundreds of fortune seekers stood around them.

Al held the paper high in the air for all to see. "I found this paper by the—" But before Al could finish his sentence, a huge falcon swooped down, ripped the paper from Al's hand, and flew away. Al was able to hold onto only a tiny shred.

"Oh, no!" the prince's assistant cried. "The map is gone. Did you look at it?" he asked Al and Gebra.

"Not really," Al said apologetically. "All I remember is that the treasure was buried in more than one place. In fact, it looked like it was buried one coin at a time in a straight line across the village."

The mood of the crowd was turning ugly. "Can't you remember where the straight line was?" one of them shouted.

"Wait," said Gebra, trying to console them. "Al still has a little piece of the map. Let's take a look at it."

Al carefully smoothed the tiny wad of paper that he had been clutching. "The straight line intercepted the Y-axis near the first cottage on South Y Street," he said, looking intently at the paper in his hands.

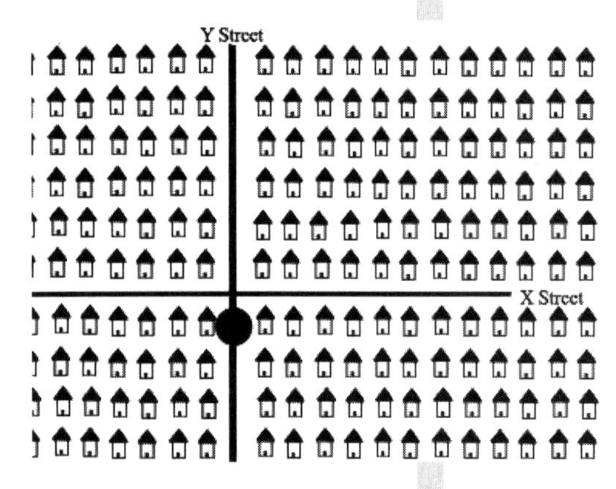

Al quickly sketched the village on a large slab of wood. "One coin was buried at the (0, -1) position on this grid. But that's all we have," he said.

A collective groan resounded throughout the fortress. "Wait a minute!" Gebra said excitedly, looking at the prince. "You said one coin had been uncovered. Where was it found?"

"It was found at my house," a woman spoke out above the crowd. "I live at (+11, +5)." Gebra marked the second point on the grid.

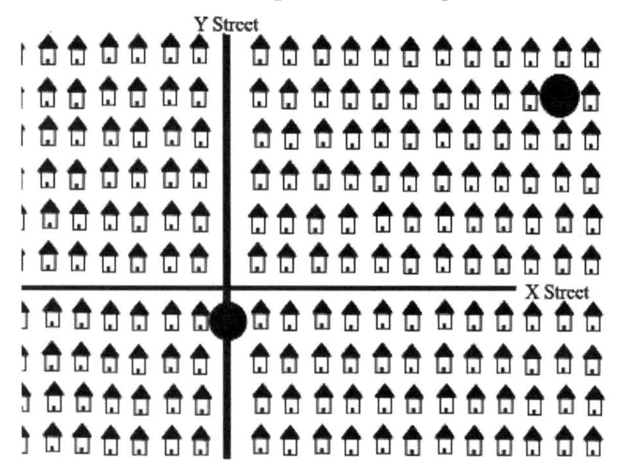

"Now we know two points on the line. If we had a huge ruler, we could draw a line through both points; then we would know exactly where the treasure is buried. But the village is too large to draw a line through, so we need to solve this problem another way," said Gebra, thinking out loud.

"We know that the formula for a straight line is Y = MX + B," said Al. "The variable B represents the Y-intercept, and we know what that is. It's negative one (-1)."

Gebra continued: "The variable M represents the slope of the line. Maybe if we solved for the slope we could figure out the rest of the formula. We know two points on the line: (0, -1) and (+11, +5)."

"The formula for the slope of a line is $\frac{Y_1 - Y_2}{X_1 - X_2}$," Al said.

"If we insert our values $\frac{(-1) - (+5)}{(0) - (+11)}$

into the formula, we know that the slope of this line is $\frac{(-6)}{(-11)}$,

or $\frac{(6)}{(11)}$." Al paused for a moment.

"Now we can substitute this value in the place of the M variable," Gebra added. "So far we have Y = (-6/-11)X + (-1)."

"What does X stand for?" a villager asked.

"X stands for the point at which the line crosses the X-axis, which will be different for each of you, according to where you live," Al explained.

"We live on -4 X Street," a small group of people said. "Where does the line cross our street?"

"If we put your street number in the place of X, we have Y = (6/11)(-4) + (-1). The line of coins crosses your street at -3.2," said Gebra after drawing in the sand.

"What about us? We live on +8 X Street," another group said.

"Y = (6/11)(8) + (-1). The line of coins crosses your street at 3.4," Al told them.

"Let's do one more of these together, then we can figure out the rest on our own," another villager suggested. "Our group lives on -9 X Street. Let's see if we can do this.

$$Y = MX + B$$
$$Y = (6/11)(-9) + (-1)$$
$$Y = (-4.95) + (-1)$$
$$Y = -5.95$$

That means the line of coins will cross our street at -5.95."

"I think you have it!" said Gebra, congratulating the villagers as one by one they returned to their streets and resumed their digging.

"How can we ever thank you?" the prince asked.

"Just remember the formula for a straight line," said Gebra, her contagious laughter ringing merrily over the multitudes.

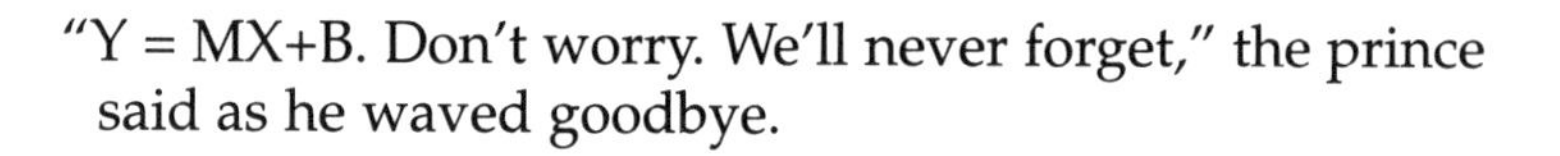

"Y = MX+B. Don't worry. We'll never forget," the prince said as he waved goodbye.

Mounting their horses and beginning to ride, Al and Gebra couldn't stop smiling as they kept hearing shouts of joy. Finally the happy sounds began fading in the distance as they made their way toward home.

The Return

Al and Gebra were stunned by an eerie stillness in their home kingdom. "Hello!" Gebra called out as they passed through the entry gate, but her greeting was answered only by the rhythm of their horses' hooves on the hard-trodden ground.

Sunlight was just beginning to filter through the crevices in the fortress wall as they paused at the door of the king's chamber. The door stood open, which was unusual, and the king sat alone on his throne at the far side of the room. Al and Gebra moved slowly through the twilight.

"Your Majesty," they said in unison as they bowed at his feet, "we are here to tell you about our journey."

"Stop!" the king answered. "It is too late."

Al and Gebra were shaken by his response. "But, Your Majesty! We have returned with answers to problems faced by each of the 14 kingdoms in our great forest, as you commanded. How can we be late?" Al asked.

"Because I already know about your journey." As the now-smiling king spoke, a red curtain fell to the floor. Behind the curtain were all of those whom Al and Gebra had met on their journey. At a signal from the king, each one shared one fact that Al and Gebra had discovered.

Real numbers less than zero are negative.

The absolute value of a positive number is the number itself.
The absolute value of a negative number is its opposite.
Examples: The absolute value of -4 is 4. The absolute value of 3 is 3.

The arithmetic mean, often called the average or simply the mean, is the sum of the values divided by the total number of values.

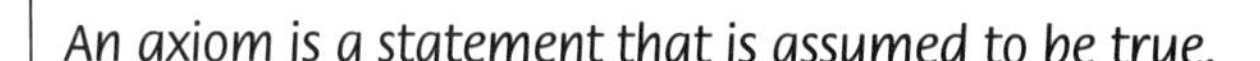

An axiom is a statement that is assumed to be true.

To add two real numbers: **If one is positive and the other negative,** find the difference of their absolute values. The result has the same sign as the addend with the greater absolute value. Examples: (+9) + (-2) = (+7); (-8) + (+5) = (-3).

If both numbers are negative, add their absolute values. The sum is negative. Example: (-6) + (-2) = (-8). **If both are positive,** add them as you always have. The sum is positive. Example: (+5) + (+1) = 6.

Theorems are statements about real numbers that can be proven to be true.

A symbol for a number, usually a letter from the Greek or English alphabet, is called a variable.

To subtract a negative number,
Listen now, no time to slumber!
Change the negative to a plus,
Then we add. How 'bout us?!
Example: (+3) – (-7) = (+10).

We're commuters.

$a + b = b + a$, and $ab = ba$.
This is the commutative axiom.

We move back and forth.

The associative property states:
(A + B) + C is the same as A + (B + C).

There are different ways to express multiplication:

$(2)(3) = 6$
$2 \times 3 = 6$
$2 \cdot 3 = 6$
ab

When multiplying and dividing signed numbers:
Opposite signs are negative, and like signs are positive.
$(+)(+) = (+)$ and $(+) \div (+) = (+)$
$(+)(-) = (-)$ and $(+) \div (-) = (-)$
$(-)(-) = (+)$ and $(-) \div (-) = (+)$
$(-)(+) = (-)$ and $(-) \div (+) = (-)$

Distributive property: $a(b + c) = ab + ac$.

Fractions and decimals live in the Kingdom of Parts.

When a mathematical sentence states that two expressions name the same number, it is an equation.

In order to keep an equation balanced, we must perform the same operations on each side.

An exponent is a number that tells how many times a factor, called the base, occurs in a product. For example, $4^3 = 4 X 4 X 4$.

A square root is a number that, when multiplied by itself, produces the given number. For example, the square root of 36 is 6.

Xy squared = X^2y^2
(a + b) squared = $(a^2 + 2ab + b^2)$

There's so much to know about squared numbers!

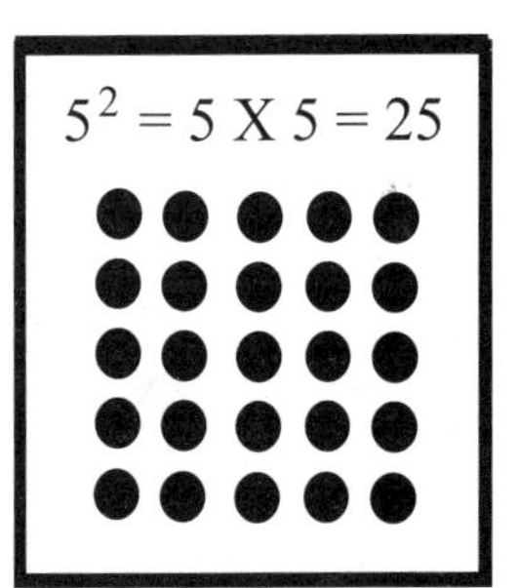

The square of a number is the product of the number and itself.

A square number looks like a square.

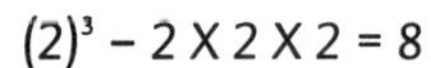

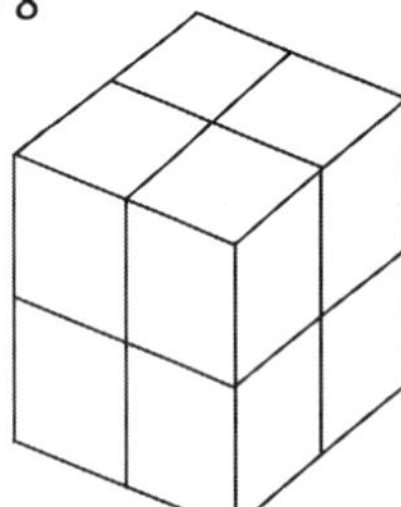

The product of a cubed number is special because it can be arranged in a cube.

Order of operation in arithmetic: parentheses, exponents, multiplication, division, addition, and subtraction. (Please Excuse My Dear Aunt Sally.)

In order to solve for X, the X variable must be isolated.

$$\frac{18 + 26 + 104 + X}{2} = 98$$

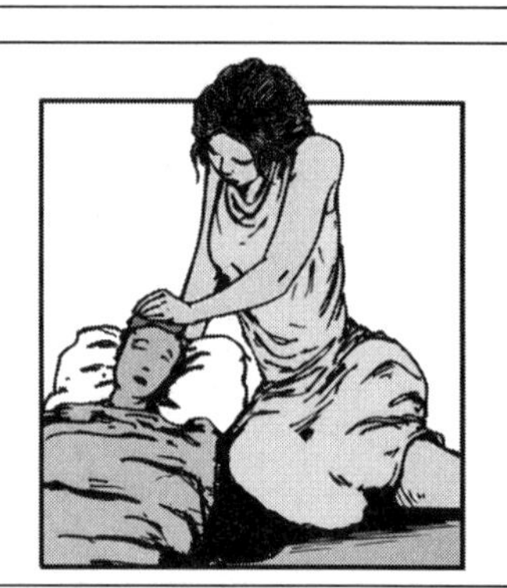

To simplify an expresson is to restate it with the simplest or most common name of its value.

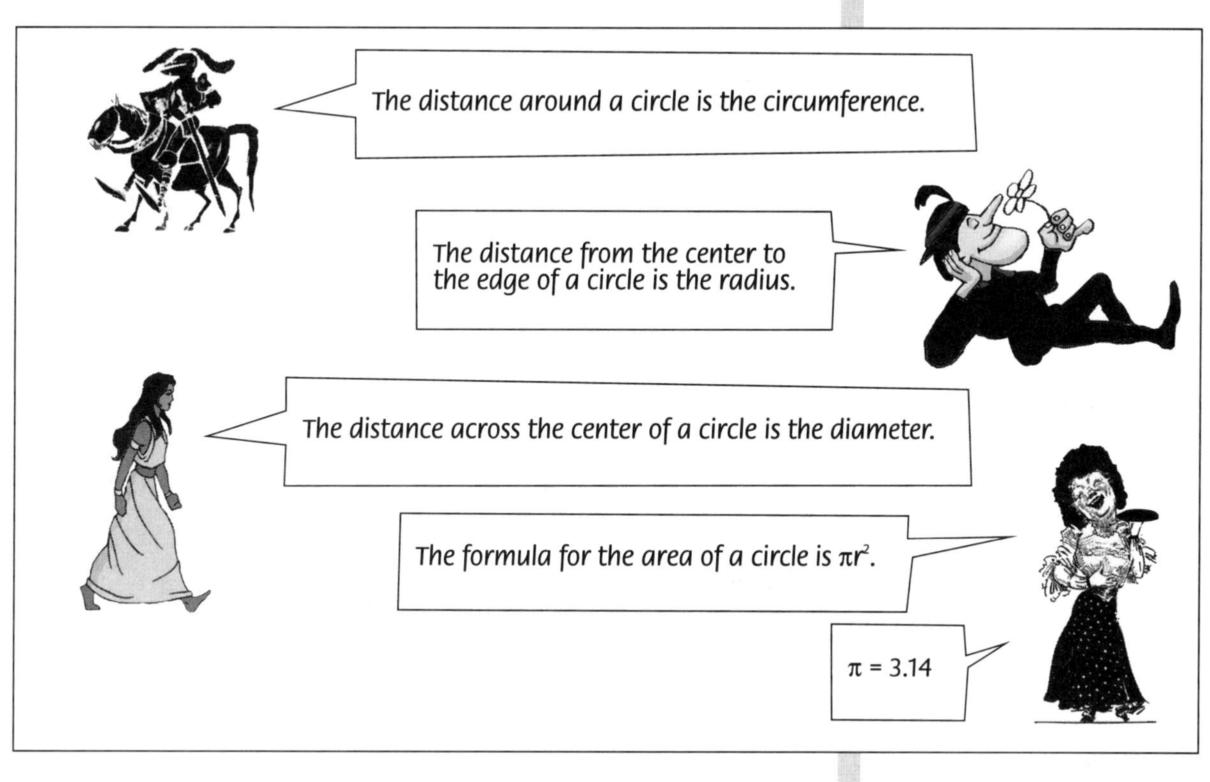

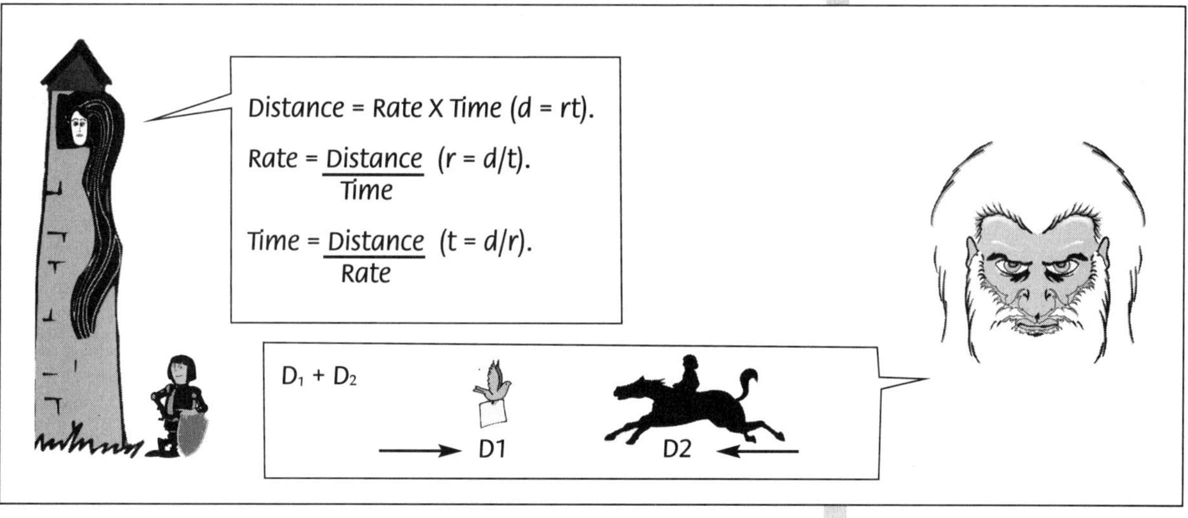

Two numbers for which the product is 1 are reciprocals. A reciprocal is also called a multiplicative inverse.

Pythagorean Theorem: For any right triangle, the square of the length of the hypotenuse equals the sum of the squares of the lengths of the legs ($a^2 + b^2 = c^2$).

A whole number greater than 1 having no whole number factors other than itself and 1 is a prime number. Examples: 3, 5, 7, 11, 13, 17, 19, 23, 27.

Numbers that can be factored are composite numbers.

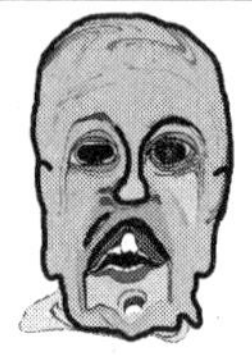

Axiom of equality: If $a = b$ and $b = c$, then $a = c$.

The first coordinate in an ordered pair is the domain, and the second one is the range.

If a relation is such that no two ordered pairs have the same first coordinate, we call the relation a function.
Example: (-2, -1) (1, 3) (-3, 0).

A relation is any set of ordered pairs. (2, -3) is an ordered pair.

The point where a line crosses the Y-axis is the Y-intercept.

$$\text{Slope} = \frac{\text{change in elevation}}{\text{change in horizontal distance}}$$

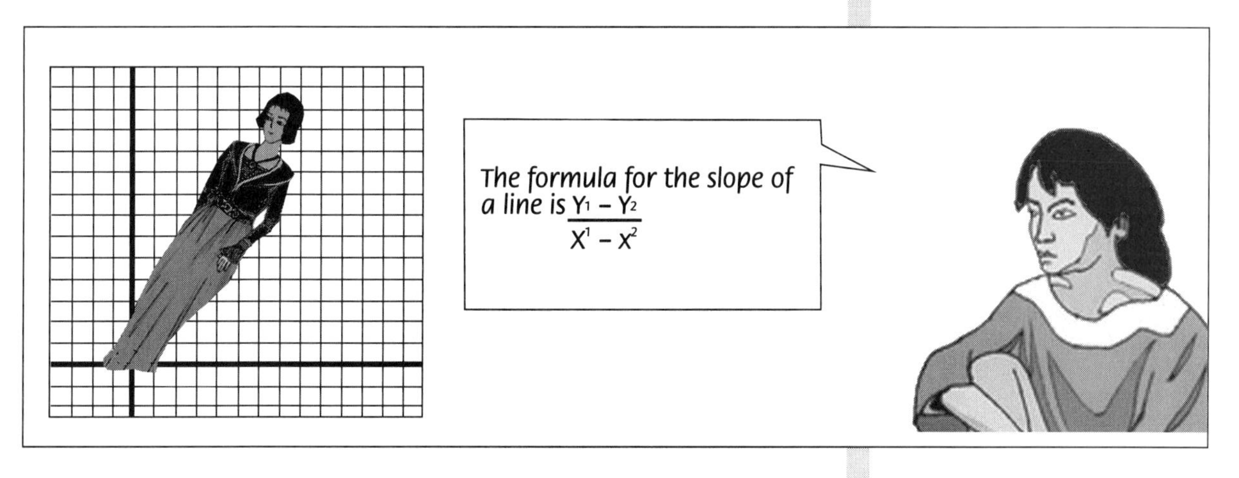

"This is no longer my kingdom," the king said, addressing the multitude, then looking gratefully at Al and Gebra. "This is now the land of Al and Gebra, and shall be called":

The Kingdom of Algebra

www.ahaprocess.com

421 Jones Road
Highlands, TX 77562-0727
(800) 424-9484
Fax (281) 426-8705

store@ahaprocess.com

ORDER FORM

Please send me: ______________ copy/copies of *Al & Gebra ...*

Books:

1-4 books $18/each + $4.50 first book, plus $2.00 each additional book shipping/handling

5 or more $15/each + 8% shipping/handling

Subtotal: $ ______________

Shipping: $ ______________

Sales tax: $ ______________

Total: $ ______________

UPS SHIP TO ADDRESS (no post office boxes, please):

Name: ______________________________

Organization: ______________________________

Address: ______________________________

____

Phone: ______________ E-mail: ______________

METHOD OF PAYMENT:

Purchase Order # ______________

Credit card type: ______________ Exp: ______________

Credit card number: ______________________________

Check: $ ______________ Check # ______________

Thanks for your order!

eye-opening
aha!
learning